LOVE SONG
FOR A
WOUNDED WARRIOR

Gift Aid

20   70785875   6029

based on a true story

Fiona and Colin Gardner

with

Andrew Gardner

British Library Cataloguing in Publication Data:
a catalogue record for this publication
is available from the British Library

ISBN: 978-1-912052-53-0

Typeset in 11.5pt Minion Pro at Haddington, Scotland

Printed by West Port Print & Design, St Andrews

CONTENTS

THE PICTURE ON THE BACK COVER IS OF 'THE SLEEPING WARRIOR'
IN THE ARRAN HILLS

FOREWORD

At the time I write, there is a much greater awareness of mental health issues. It is so important that we support people to get the diagnosis, treatment and support that they need to become well. There can still be shame and stigma around trauma, brain damage and mental health issues which make it difficult for people to ask for help. I see many people who live with these issues every day, folk who are weary and feeling overwhelmed.

This book is the story of a veteran who suffered from the symptoms of post traumatic stress, epilepsy, brain damage and their consequences. How can we as a society better care for veterans and their families? This is not a political book, rather it just tells a story of the joys and the unpleasant complexities and ambiguities of life with a veteran who struggled with his identity after injury on active service. There are many other stories out there, many other families of veterans who suffer trauma vicariously. We need to hear their voices, and support one another as a community. Colin asked me to tell his story, and I hope this will remind others that they do not struggle alone: there is help out there.

Jesus showed compassion to the suffering and the marginalised:

> 'Compassion asks us to go where it hurts, to enter into the places of pain, to share in brokenness, fear, confusion, and anguish . . . Compassion requires us to be weak with the weak, vulnerable with the vulnerable, and powerless with the powerless. Compassion means full immersion in the condition of being human.' *

Compassion builds bridges of understanding, and can help us in our quest for wholeness and peace and rest. May God's compassion for us help us find the ability to forgive and be forgiven, and offer opportunities for grace and reconciliation.

Fiona Gardner, March 2020

---

* Henri J. M. Nouwen, 'You are the Beloved: Daily Meditations for Spiritual Living', Hachette UK, 2017.

EDVARD MUNCH, *THE SCREAM* (CREDIT: NATIONAL MUSEUM OF NORWAY)

This book is dedicated to veterans and their families,
and all who suffer as a result of conflict. May their voices be heard,
and may they find the healing they seek.

All proceeds from this book will be divided
between two Glasgow Charities:

Epilepsy Connections and *The Coming Home Centre*

We are delighted to support these inspirational Charities, but this does
not mean that either Charity endorses the contents of this book.

If Colin's story can in any way support others who struggle or suffer,
then this helps to give what we are doing purpose.

INTRODUCTION

'To be a person you have to have a story to tell.'
   Isak Dinesen

'Gather up the fragments that remain, that nothing be lost.'
   John 6:12

'Only connect . . .'
   E.M. Forster (*Howard's End*)

The man in the corner of the café was drinking his soup. He looked to be middle aged, unshaven, unremarkable, casually dressed. He moved slowly but enthusiastically on to his next course – a 'big breakfast' with fried eggs and sausages and bacon and tomatoes and mushroom and black pudding and toast. He chewed away methodically at every morsel, and relished each bite, even taking time to scrape the residue off the plate, until at the end he stopped, satisfied and well fed. He looked up, and you could not help but notice his beautiful brown eyes, deep and compelling. He sat with his friend, quietly, savouring a cup of tea, to wash the avalanche of food into his stomach.

He looks like just another person, someone who would blend into a crowd, with nothing particularly noticeable or different. And yet, like every human being, he has his story, a story to tell of his life, particularly of his time in active military service, and then the impact that this time had on the rest of his life. This book is going to try to tell his story – as much as any human life can ever be conveyed in words on a page. I tell part of Colin's story from my perspective, as his wife – the perceptions of a carer. I work full time from home, and am someone who travelled alongside with Colin for part of the way. I am a Christian minister, which has meant times of questioning, of struggle with what life means, how to cope with pain and heartache when I believe in a loving and gracious God. I give the narrative framework for what takes place, if you like I provide the basket for the fragments to be gathered.

Then in various places, Colin tells of his experiences in his own words, of some of the things that he did, the places he went to, the feelings he had. His voice is sometimes tender and thoughtful, but often raw, strident, abrasive. He is looking at the very immediate issues that he faced – giving descriptions in prose and poetry of his experiences, particularly of his time of service in the military, in the intelligence corps of the army. His experiences are recalled with meticulous attention to detail – the adrenalin – seems to have seared them into his soul.

Some details are more impressionistic in nature, others have been modified to protect identities – past and present – e.g. the names of nearly all individuals have been changed. The essence of the memories have been preserved however, and shared in good faith. Some of Colin's memories are uncomfortably painful and caustic, but they need to be recalled because they are the kind of experiences that so many who serve in the armed services have to endure. They need to be heard, so that the patterns of trauma, guilt and rage that so many experience is recognised, unpleasant haunting memories which can maim the character, scar the soul and completely devastate relationships.

I have struggled with how to tell this story – of my wounded warrior – for in the end all our stories are both individual and universal, in the past and yet imminently present, incredibly personal and profoundly entangled, so that it is hard to tell the end from the beginning. Some of Colin's memories are included in 'flashback' form, as he lived both the present and the past simultaneously, which is often part of a veteran's legacy. These memories are long ago, but also can erupt violently and abruptly into the present, like an unbidden volcano, showering scalding debris over all who are nearby.

Thank you for reading this. We are honoured that you seek to do so, and pray that it will encourage all of us to persevere through life, and always to treat others with dignity and respect and compassion for we need to respect every voice and to validate every story.

How did this book come to be written? Well, for many years my husband wanted to write a book about his experiences. In the past, he wrote poems to help describe some of the military episodes in his life. He wrote episodes recalling events, which he wanted to join together into a narrative. Yet towards the end of his life, he was not well enough to do this – to recall the framework for the details, or to put his life into words, so I feel compelled to tell his story, our story, and to fill in the missing spaces, to bring the pieces together in such a way that they make sense to another living human being outside our immediate family.

In some ways we are like every other family – husband, wife and son, living out our lives. Paradoxically at the same time, our life is bizarre, incomprehensible, unusual, excruciating, traumatic, nonsensical and hilarious – often simultaneously! Yet in the midst of it all there is an internal cohesion which merits discovery. It is a story of the human spirit, body, mind and soul – fighting for survival, fighting for identity, for validation. It is a universal condition – where every person seeks to define their personhood, and yet I would humbly like to offer the story of one couple in their quest for meaning. There are many amazing moments on the journey – with people we have met, places we have been, with God along the way, and we would like to record these, and to encourage others that there is meaning in all things.

In the 1982 film *Bladerunner*, one of the artificial life forms Roy makes a speech. He has attacked and killed people during his rather violent existence. However, as his life fades away, he calmly sits and delivers a soliloquy about the experiences of his life:

> 'I've seen things you people wouldn't believe. Attack ships on fire off the shoulder of Orion. I watched C-beams glitter in the dark near the Tauhauser Gate. All those moments will be lost in time, like tears in rain . . . Time to die.'

It is our wish that Colin's life should not disappear like teardrops in the rain, and that something might be remembered, that his experiences might have some significance for others. The idea of the poet Wordsworth is that there are 'spots of time' that have an eternal significance. Every encounter in life can be significant, even when that meaning is not immediately apparent, an opportunity for compassion and grace to be shown.

Someone has said that integration leads to wholeness and to healing This book is a story of an ongoing journey to integration. It hopefully demonstrates the interconnectedness of all things – war and peace, faith and secular, physical and psychological. We create and define barriers between different sections of experience, but there is a complex system of bridges between them which defies compartmentalism. Some of the details of events are absent from these accounts, others are recorded as perceptions, hinting only the impression that they left, rather than this being a detailed blow by blow factual history. Many names and some places have been changed to keep people safe. And yet the essence of this narrative is true, and we hope that this is an evocation of the complexity of the human condition – and the way that God can help human beings survive in its midst, with dignity and grace.

It is written for others to have insight as to how issues of war, broken trust and disability and ill health can impact on a life, and to have more understanding and compassion towards those whose faces do not fit. For people in the medical profession, who are sometimes tempted to see everyone as another number, I would love you to read this to understand how it can feel to be on the other side of the system. We are very grateful for all the help that we have received from the NHS, and we have met a number of outstanding individuals along the way, but we offer this account of our experiences as a tool for reflection and learning.

I have included some medical details in this account, and there is a glossary at the back of the book, to help with any technical terms. Colin often didn't respond to treatment as he was meant to, and this led to many times of anguish. For all relatives who strive to find understanding of their loved one's condition, we identify with your frustrations. Sometimes too, relatives need to speak up, to go with their gut feelings about what might be right for their loved one, and to keep repeating this until it is listened to. Detailed matters of medication and treatment are of such great importance for everyday wellbeing and dignity, whilst to some doctors and nurses, they can seem trivial details that can be casually overlooked.

'When you have suffered a great deal in life, each additional pain is both unbearable and trifling.' *

This sums up so much of life, which is both small and epic simultaneously. After a while, the danger is that you become so desensitised, that you question if you can still discern the proportionality of it all, yet we move forward with hope.

Colin used to love quotations, and so I have included some which hopefully illuminate something of our predicament. Many of Colin's poems are included – the dates that they are written and revised were often long after the event, for he went over them again and again. Our journey has been gruelling, yet with moments of great joy and laughter in the sadness. Yet telling the story is necessary, and helps us all recognise that we are in solidarity with one another, and this somehow brings purpose.

---

* Yann Martel, *The Life of Pi*, Knopf 2001.

ACKNOWLEDGEMENTS

I think being a carer for someone with a progressive neurological disease, can mean you feel very much alone at times. But Andrew and I have also felt so privileged to have had wonderful support, and we want to acknowledge our grateful thanks to all those who have prayed for us, and supported us, and surrounded us with their love.

We want to say an enormous thank you to my mum and Colin's parents, who were stunning in their support for us, and who spent much time in the house caring for Andrew when he was growing up. Some days were not easy, but you were all superb! We want to thank all those in the broader family also, for their support and care, as well as our faithful dogs Todd and Jack!

And to Bill as an incredibly faithful, generous and understanding companion and visitor and friend to Colin, to Diane for her understanding and care in unusual situations, and to Neil for his quiet wisdom and support of all of us.

A great big thank you to Sally and to Jim, for their depth of love and support over so many years, for Sally typing up Colin's writings with such attention and thoughtfulness, and for Muriel's consistent and generous prayers and loving insights and encouragement.

A wonderful thank you to Evelyn, as Andrew's Nanny, who was also appreciative of Colin's humour and dry wit, and who shared the good times and the bad. A grateful thanks to Iain and Robert for their care and shared sense of humour with Colin! And to wonderful friends – Lynn and John, Lesli, Margaret and David, Margaret B and Jenny, the Book Group, Gail, Alan and Clare, Margie and David and so many others.

An enormous thank you to Johanna and David, their family and friends, for wonderful compassion and prayerful understanding, for their incredible hospitality and their ability to laugh and cry with us over so many years.

To colleagues Fergus, David and Margaret for pastoral care over the years.

To the medical staff who took the time to listen to Colin, and to give him the best care, even in the most demanding and humorous situations!

Grateful thanks to all who helped us along the road, including Marianne and Robin at the Bield at Blackruthven, Alison at the Ignatian centre, Myra, and also Anna Potter – cranial osteopath.

To Eileen and her team at Craigielea care home, for making Colin's final years the best they could be, for making him feel at home, enjoying his jokes, understanding his frustrations, and counting his entire dvd collection when he asked! For being ok with him taking two hours to eat a meal, and letting him stack the medicine beakers so he could fill them with rind from his bacon to feed the birds.

An enormous thank you to everyone who read this manuscript, including Shirley G, Marianne, Muriel, Johanna and David, Linda and Sandy, Brian, Brian M, Alison, Shirley M, Gabby, Allana, David and our family for their encouragement.

An enormous thank you to Trevor Royle, who has listened sympathetically and given me so much guidance, and to Norman for his help, to Rosemary for her wise counsel and care, and to Campbell for his helpful insights, and to Ian and Cindy for their support and helpful advice.

And to my editor and publisher Jock Stein, for his careful editing, much patience and thought, as he prepared this book and brought it all together in its current form – amazing!

Fiona Gardner

Chapter 1

COLIN'S EARLIER LIFE
(IN HIS OWN WORDS)

Colin was born on 9th September 1956 to Tom and Audrey Gardner, in Thornwood in Glasgow. He had a big brother Thomas. The family had cats – Ashes and Tiger. Colin's cat was Ashes. Even as a small boy, Colin was adorable!

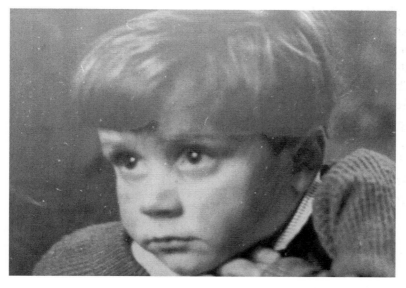

And in his school work, he loved drawing pictures of battles and planes. He was always a bit of a rebel, and wondered what he would do with his life. He was an intelligent boy, proud of taking on the school bully, and he had a heart for justice. Colin learned the violin at school, but he did not excel at this; one of his cousins said he was the only person she knew that could do such good impersonations of *The Clangers* with the violin!

Colin wrote an outline of his early years, and his time in the military, which follows.

TIMELINE OF KEY EVENTS as I (Colin) remember them

1972 – left school at 16 years, 7 'O' levels, 3 'highers'.

1972/3 – Obtained first job as Lab Technician at Glasgow University with team doing 'medical research into skin disease of the foot' Did ONC at Bell College of Technology.

1973 – Started HNC at Bell College. Becoming bored with current job as it was very repetitive.

MILITARY

Visited army recruitment centre – initially not many convincing suggestions, until I noted a poster on the wall with a large 'eye'. I asked the sergeant what the reference was. He replied, 'Intelligence Corp, Military Intelligence but if I knew anything about them I probably wouldn't be allowed to tell you,' and smiled. I was hooked. A visit from somebody at military intelligence was arranged, and I consented to 'signing on' at 9 September 1973, age 18 (newly).

1973 Now in Army Intelligence Corp, sent to School of Military Intelligence. Ashford in Kent for recruitment training. 1 years training.

1974 First posting – Northern Ireland 12 Int and Sy Coy, Belfast. Initially attached to various regular army patrols to 'observe'. 6 months with English Regiment eventually becoming their Chief. Sometimes on riot control if the unit I was with was assigned to this duty. Transferred to SMIU Special Military Intelligence Unit. The first six months were on phone tapping. Initially the subjects were varied with terrorist info. the aim. Later subjects were councillors and MPs with aim to record any unusual conversations.

1975 Assigned to the Regional Crime Squad (RUC) in converted old army barracks in the town of Armagh in South Armagh County. Area was nicknamed 'bandit country' due to the amount of terrorist activity and close proximity to the Irish Border. I was part of the first Regional Crime Squad to be formed in Northern Ireland. I now had authority to carry a gun at all times (on leave), anywhere in the UK. My training in photography at Ashford was used by the RCS. In the darkroom, did developing and printing according to requests. Used on surveillance operations and also to record scenes of incidents. It meant that I was a witness to a lot of shootings, petrol bombings and car bombings.

The work overall involved investigations, enquiries, assisting other officers, surveillance operations, working with local SAS units, suspect interrogations, court prosecution.

Work meant I got insufficient sleep, and a photograph of me shows very dark lines under the eyes, with my face sagging. When going on leave to Britain, the I.D. I carried was refused at the entry desk because the official said that I was too old to be the person on the photograph on the I.D. I was age 19 but the official thought that I was 35.

CAR CRASH

Returning early in the morning from Belfast, I fell asleep whilst driving. The car rolled into a field and was totally destroyed. On return to consciousness I managed to crawl out of the car into the field, but any attempts to stand up proved to be futile as my mind was in a total spin and I would immediately collapse. I continued to persist and eventually succeeded. Somehow I managed to stagger back to the barracks in Armagh although any observer would assume I was absolutely blitzed on alcohol from the way I persistently staggered all over the road. At the barracks the guards initially refused me entry believing I was drunk. I also had some cuts that required stitched, and was able to show the guards a blood covered hand from one of the wounds on my back. The guards believed my accident story and called an ambulance. An x-ray of my head showed the right side to be black, presumably from internal bleeding. Although I was very fortunate in not having any immediate after-effects or seizures (not for five years anyway), since the accident I have never had another headache.

PETROL BOMB

In response to a Fire Brigade call a colleague and myself were sent to check on an incident, the location of which appeared to be one the RCS were currently investigating. At the scene, the fire brigade were already trying to control a fire in two warehouses. The Police and soldiers in the area together with the overall condition of the streets gave the impression that possible crowd control may have been used. We established who the owners of the warehouses were, and what their contents were supposed to be. Parked on the far side of the town square, we gave a brief summary of the situation over the radio.

During this time, an individual had crept along the side of the car. He stood up at my open side window, called a very brief statement about 'freedom from repression' and lobbed the burning petrol bomb through the open window. I immediately ducked and the bomb lodged itself between my back and the car seat. Presumably because of the cushioning effect of the seat, the bottle neither broke or exploded, enabling my colleague to grab and throw it out of my car. The bottle smashed on the street, and burned itself out. The only obvious damage was a few scorch marks on the seat, and some burn marks to the back of the sheepskin jacket that I had recently bought. The individual responsible had already run into a side alley/lane, and was not apprehended.

FEBRUARY 1978 LEAVE NORTHERN IRELAND

Left RCS Squad and was reassigned 'fitness training' with Army Unit in Wales for three months. Apart from general fitness, the majority of the training was provided by Special Air Services (SAS). On completion of training, instructions were given to fly to Belize where a new assignment would be issued. Guatemala (six months). On arrival in Belize I was met by another intelligence individual whom I recognised from first training days at Ashford. He explained the operation was essentially SAS (30 in total, three units of 10) with one member of Intelligence to each unit of 10. Tripped over US forces working for G. National Army. Caused falling out between US/UK Government. US forces were making an example of Indian villages. Eventually scared US off.

1979 ANTI TERRORIST BRANCH

Assigned to assist Metropolitan Police for six months, no obvious explanation provided. On arrival at New Scotland Yard building, I presented myself to the security desk and was informed someone would be down. I was taken to the Offices of the Anti-Terrorist Branch and introduced to some of the personnel and the team I was to work with. Due to information about PIRA setting up various operations in London a request for additional officers to SMIU had meant a number of reassignments at short notice. Working with the teams involved checking pubs, cafes, all known sources, any info that came in, but generally all those with Army connections like myself, would follow the instructions of the nearest Police Officers. Initially we were regarded as something like SAS/Supermen, but within a few weeks relations had sufficiently softened that additional personnel were considered an integrated part of their teams.

SNLA REASSIGNMENT TO INT & SP COY, EDINBURGH

Whilst working with my new assignment, I obtained contact with a Scottish Terrorist Group SNLA (Scottish National Liberation Army). The group was still in its early stages with no previous history of operations on record. Forming on the same patterns as the PIRA used, members obtained tuition and training from the IRA in Ireland. The IRA were very supportive to the SNLA, interpretation of their intended activities was seen as a kind of 'Second Front' to N.I. and therefore to be encouraged. Initial info on SNLA was well received by seniors. I received orders to cancel any other work and to concentrate on gaining access to SNLA and any info about their activities/intentions/names.

I became a member of SNLA and later the 1980 operation was expanded to include the Special Branch of Strathclyde, Central and Lothian Police forces. Special Branch are regarded the 'Intelligence' part of police activities, although the reference is more often considered a 'contradiction in terms'.

Already working under a cover name for security, I met representatives of all three forces Special Branch in an arranged meeting at Harthill Service Station on the A8. Ensuring I arrived prior to the police in order to witness their arrival and judge for myself what they would be like to work with, I was not initially impressed. Apart from being easy to identify as police due to each individual's height and haircut, contact with me was made by calling out my cover name across the room. I continued to work with the police until the conclusion of the operation in early 1981 with the conviction of nine members of SNLA under the Anti-Terrorist Act and several others for minor offences. 1980 Anti-Terrorist Branch. Whilst at Edinburgh I was assigned to assist the Anti-Terrorist at their special request. Similar to the previous operation in 1979, teams were to comb streets in preparation for a Queens's parade through part of London. Work lasted six weeks.

On return to Edinburgh, I continued with the SNLA. Promotion to Sergeant. Sent on a training course for promotion to Sergeant. On route to England, I stopped to stay overnight with an old girlfriend. Because I was to report for duty at 8.00am at Ashford, I had to leave very early in the morning, which meant practically no sleep that night. I successfully reached Ashford in time and started the training course without delay. Having missed a few meals in the last few days, by the end of the afternoon, I was looking forward to a good dinner and an early bed.

I was informed that we were actually intended for a five night exercise of physical training. Each individual was to follow a specified route, collecting ten marked packages at various locations. Each package would require the individual to successfully perform an unspecified task/function/test. If any were unsuccessful, the package would not be handed over. Seven of the packages were considered necessary for a pass. That night I managed to collect eight of the packages, but as I was approaching the final location I experienced dizziness and was seen to stagger. In an attempt to assist me, headlights of vehicles were switched on. They dazzled me instead, making me feel worse, and I shortly collapsed. I was taken to hospital and diagnosed as collapsed due to exhaustion. Blood tests showed practically no evidence of sugar in my blood. Taken off the course, and I was put on sick leave.

Returned to Edinburgh and continued with the SNLA. When the police arrested members of the SNLA, wives and girlfriends were also charged with the same offences. Due to my close contact with the SNLA, I knew that the men adhered to a strict rule of not sharing any info with their wives/girlfriends other than basic details about the group. Any time the men visited Ireland for some training, the women would be left behind without any knowledge of the location of the men or a date for their return. Examination of the evidence used when making the charges satisfied me as being false/fabricated. In conversation with police involved with the arrest I made clear about the women not being guilty of the same offences as the men. This was at first regarded as some kind of joke, but when I threatened to expose the evidence to the press, my intentions were questioned and taken more seriously. The charges against the women were reduced from anti-terrorist act to other minor offences. I shortly after received a visit to my flat from three men wearing balaclavas and boiler suits, who forced entry at my open door. After a few futile attempts to fight at the door, I was knocked to the floor, and my head repeatedly kicked.

I shortly afterwards lost consciousness. I have no means of identifying the visitors other than they were all very professional with the skills of unarmed combat. Who sent them – of this I can never be sure. I was taken to hospital where I regained consciousness, and received treatment and a few stitches. As soon as I was mobile, I was transferred to a location in Wales for safety and recuperation.

Afterwards, I was medically discharged from the service, my injuries – the condition of epilepsy – listed as received on active service.

During my military career, I never received any counselling/debriefing after extreme events. I was never supposed to tell anyone about my activities / work.

Later, I received a phone call from a person who explained that he had been instructed to clean out my files removing any evidence of intelligence ops, destroy anything about work with SMIU/MI5/SAS and all details about my involvement with the SNLA in Edinburgh. He was to leave only general references and dates of assignments and their locations e.g. 12 Int and Sy Coy Belfast. With no other information about activities in NI. The same was for all other assignments and years.

CIVILIAN (SUMMARY)

1981–87   Did degree at Glasgow University in Social Science subjects (MA). In first year, did well with the subjects that I took and was to receive a number of exemptions. Then I began to have frequent seizures and had to take a number of years out whilst they tried to find medication to control my epilepsy. This was a very intense period and my seizures seemed to get worse year by year, and I felt sure that I would end up dying.

On one occasion, my medication reacted with my body defences, and provoked destruction of oxygen carrying cells in my body. Day by day I lost more of my mind and by the end of the week, I had already lost too much to react about it. I eventually collapsed and was taken to hospital, where I remained having fantasies about terrorists having poisoned my food, and moving around the building, trying to get access to attack me. I refused any food or drink for three days and eventually recovered consciousness.

1988   With epilepsy reasonably well controlled (night time seizures only), started work at Illegal Money Lending Unit, due to help from a friend; I was suggested as a possible to assist with the setting up of the Unit for Strathclyde Regional Council. I was to construct a dark room and obtain all necessary materials for photographic printing and processing. I was also to advise the Unit as to techniques and methods for surveillance.

Colin Gardner

Chapter 2

OUR FIRST MEETING –
COLIN AT THE BUTCHER'S SHOP!

'A journey of a thousand miles must begin with a single step.'

Tao Ta Ching

In 1989, I was a part-time student and needed to earn some money. I got a job as assistant at a butcher's shop. I served the customers, enjoyed the banter and getting to know them. It was 20 hours a week – a long time to be on your feet, and I had another job too, as well as being a student! Working at the shop, I didn't have to cut any meat – using the knives looked kind of tricky. Yet the longer I worked in the shop there the more I recognised the artistry with which everything was done, and the precision and knowledge that lay behind carving a 'good cut of meat'. Maybe this was a metaphor for all things, for even in the midst of the rawness of life, something beautiful is present.

There were many interesting customers – people who were sad, or had a laugh, people who were chatty, people who were focussed only on the task in hand – getting their steak pie. It was a busy shop, and there was never a dull moment. The staff were friendly, and it worked out well. At the end of the day, you could get a bag of chips from the fish and chip shop over the road, and eat them on the way home – chips always taste better outside, especially on a cold winter evening.

I don't remember the first time that he came in the shop. I just remembered that he bought rather a lot of mince. He kept coming back – a man perhaps in his early thirties, not very tall, a muscular build, and with a beard. He had brown eyes. He talked about different topics, and one day he asked me out for a coffee. This was not why I was working in the butcher's shop – to meet men, and I was a bit taken aback, but I thought why not – what's a coffee in the overall scheme of things. We met and kept meeting talking over every topic in the universe, or so it seemed.

It was a bright day on which we met for coffee, it just looked like any other day. Yet it wasn't the same as any other – for it was the first day that Colin started to share some of his story with me. It turned out that he had been in the military, in Northern Ireland in the 1970's. He had served in the Intelligence services, and had lots of stories to tell – stories of car bombs and the death of small children, of having to tell the next of kin, of being shot and shooting others, and of the haunting guilt of it all. It was like walking into another world. In the dark and murky world that he described, his role always seemed to be honourable: trying to do the right thing in impossible circumstances. He told the stories with intensity and conviction and pride and sorrow – every detail symbolic of something else – another emotional nuance or a different perspective. As time went on, he told the same stories again and again – every time with the same attention to detail and the same narrative sequence, as if the adrenalin of the events had seared such memories eternally in his heart and mind forever.

A story of exhilaration and excitement that Colin was very proud of, was a memory of a parachute jump:

High Altitude Fall

It's your first time attempting such a jump, you're an absolute beginner, your colleagues from the SAS who helped you train and practise, were all practised experts but still it is not enough – you know you are nervous as hell and feeling a bit queasy about this first time if you're honest with yourself. Yes, you have done parachute jumps before and thought you were quite practised, but never anything like this with a high altitude fall where you must time 30 seconds precisely on the high altitude computer attached to your wrist, before opening the only possible life saving device you've got – your parachute.

You can be sure it will be the longest 30 seconds in your entire life, but have you considered how much speed you can accumulate in 30 seconds of falling? And suppose you were to hit another object, another bird, a passing plane, after all, you're only wearing a helmet for safety reasons. In 30 seconds you'll fall over three miles (providing you fall directly) – with your legs tucked in and your arms not too far outstretched, where you can see every second of the thirty seconds fall on the high altitude computer on your left wrist. But if you panic, and open your parachute too early it's all lost. The SAS won't look at you a second time. Just remember you're falling through the air at approximately 360mh. Imagine if you just hit a bird at that speed, no it wouldn't disintegrate, it would probably help tear your arm off – hence the importance of falling correctly. And after the first jump the others become increasingly easier. Well that's what they said about parachute jumps and you believed it, but nobody had told you about 'high altitude falls.'

At 0.00 hrs, the red light was on and the door opened in preparation for the jump. 10 seconds later the green light was on and I stepped out the open door and felt the first pressure of wind as I increasingly gained speed and the air swirled about my body as if it was teasing me or just being playful. After all, 30 seconds later I would be asking the same air to save my life.

Colin talked about many things. We went out and had a meal, he made food, and he was a good cook. He lived in a flat, and he was interested in politics – the Scottish Constitutional convention and the SNP, in American foreign policy and opera and all kinds of things. He worked as an Authorised Officer in the Trading Standards Department, and enjoyed trying to help the public. He had to interpret complicated laws, and to relate to consumers when they brought their complaints. He did weights and calibration testing at garages and pubs. His job had lots of variety. He loved Scotland, and going out for walks, and we did some gentle hill-climbing together (gentle due to me not being very fit). Colin had a very good friend that he went mountaineering with, and there were lots of photos of Colin up snowy mountains with crampons and an ice-axe.

We talked and talked – conversations about life, what it was all about, its purpose. We talked about Colin's near death experience in an ambulance when he had been unwell, and about the existence of God. He was a deeply spiritual person, with a real sense of the importance of justice. He was a good listener, and had a really philosophical brain – he liked to think. Through the grace of God, Colin became a Christian and started going to church. He liked the revolutionary aspect of Jesus' teaching, about the need for there to be values in life, a right and a wrong beyond human mistakes and misunderstandings. He liked the concept of grace and forgiveness, that there could be a life beyond this one, which would be beautiful and good.

As the years passed, we became good friends. Colin was patient with me, and listened to my own story, and who I was. He was good at listening, and being still, giving me space to be myself. I was on my own voyage of self-discovery, and I needed that space. As time went on, we became romantically involved, and our relationship was based on mutual understanding and trust. Our shared Christian faith made an enormous difference too, and it was wonderful to see Colin baptised in the church that we went to. It was a great thing for him to know that he was loved by God, that his sins were forgiven, and that he had a new start in life.

At one time, I went to Belfast for three months to do some voluntary work, and Colin came over to visit. At that time in the early 1990s, there were still soldiers and armoured vehicles on the streets. It took some time for me to get used to the atmosphere there, that when you were out walking down a city street, groups of soldiers trained their guns on you as part of their regular routine. Your bag was searched by soldiers every time you went to a shopping centre. The hotel along the road was always in a state of repair after the most recent bomb. Belfast was a place of friendship and laughter and 'craic' as they called it, but was also riven with such deep wounds and scars in relationships, in family and community life. (People used to keep inviting me to go to the pub to have some crack, and it took me a while to work out that they weren't all on drugs, but rather they wanted some banter!).

Being in Belfast, helped me to understand Colin's stories better. I was involved in cross community work in the city, as a volunteer – very much on the margins, yet it gave me an insight into the deep rooted tensions between Protestant and Catholic Communities, as well as the excellent work some of the churches were doing to work for reconciliation and peace. I went to the Presbyterian church there – Fitzroy, and loved its atmosphere of compassion and thoughtful and lively Christian witness.

When Colin came over, we went down to Bray, and enjoyed some time in Dublin. It brought back some memories for him from his time in the intelligence services in the past.

WEEKEND IN DUBLIN

Myself and three other RCS officers had taken a weekend off to spend some time in Dublin. On return to Armagh, we were caught in traffic queues on the wrong side of the border. The reason for the traffic disruption was a PIRA collection. Individuals wearing balaclavas presenting collection tins through open windows with the statement 'donations for the cause'. One of my colleagues, just back from Spain, took the collection tin and started to make a big donation of coins which greatly impressed the terrorist. What the terrorist and the other occupants of the car did not realise, was that the coins were actually pesetas our colleague had brought back from his holiday in Spain. On confessing this info to the others, we just about flipped, and prayed that they wouldn't open the collection tins till after the traffic had started to move, and that they would not come back to check our IDs. My colleague who was still showing evidence of having too much to drink in Dublin, had now greatly fallen from favour. His unpopularity lessened with the northern side of the border, and laughing about the incident ensued.

There were times when Colin seemed a bit tense about some of this, but mostly he was fine. I had also found out a bit about Colin's disability from his military days – he had epilepsy, but only had seizures when he was asleep, and they did not seem to affect him too badly. Colin had grand mal seizures, and sometimes after a seizure, he seemed a bit groggy or a bit down, but it soon passed. He shared with me a bit of his medical story. Colin had been injured a number of times on active service – in a car crash, being shot, and then just before he was discharged out of the army, from a beating he had received. After the latter injury, he had developed epilepsy. That was the reason given for his leaving the army – epilepsy – on his discharge papers.

He started off having occasional seizures, however his condition worsened when he was at University. He did a degree in Social Sciences, and liked to relate how well he did in first year, getting exemptions and enjoying the benefits of being an older student. He loved subjects such as philosophy and economics and modern politics. Then his epilepsy became less well controlled, and his seizures became more frequent. Colin lived with his mum and dad. He became very down because of his seizures, and this meant that he started to have a drink or two with his pal to ease the pain of it all. This didn't help, but the sorrow and frustration of having seizures and such so many black memories from the past took their toll. It took the doctors years to sort out a balance in Colin's medication and eventually his GP suggested a different anti-convulsant, and at last this one – epanutin – worked. Colin was able to start rebuilding his life.

After 7 long years at university, the prolonged time period due to all the seizures, Colin was able to finish his degree, and to start looking for work. He got his driving licence back. With his military background and training, he got a job creating a photography unit to develop pictures of illegal money lenders in the city, and he did this job so ably, that he was offered a job as an Authorised Officer in the Trading Standards Department. It was at this point in Colin's life that I met him in the butcher's shop.

Certificate of Service

Army No. 24327916
Surname GARDNER
Christian or Fore Name(s) COLIN SCARLE
Enlisted at GLASGOW
Enlisted on 3 OCTOBER 1974
Corps for which enlisted INTELLIGENCE CORPS

Description of Soldier on leaving Army Service

Date of Birth 9 SEPTEMBER 1956 Height 5 ft 5 ins cm
Complexion FRESH Eyes BROWN Hair BROWN
Marks and Scars (visible) NIL Blood Group O POS

Warning

If this certificate be lost or mislaid no duplicate can be obtained. Should, however, loss be due to exceptional circumstances, a certificate, on Army Form B108A, may be obtained on application to the Officer in Charge, Manning and Records concerned.

The person to whom this Certificate is issued must on no account part with it, or forward it by post when applying for a situation, a copy should be used.

Any alteration of the particulars given in this Certificate may render the holder liable to prosecution.

Soldiers on leaving Her Majesty's Service are hereby reminded that the unauthorised communication by them to another person at any time of any information they may have acquired which might be useful to any enemy in War renders them liable to prosecution under the Official Secrets Acts.

Army Form B.108 (Revised 12/75)

Assessment of Military Conduct and Character

(This page to be entirely free from erasure)

Military Conduct EXEMPLARY.

Note The Range of Military Conduct Gradings possible is:—
(1) Exemplary (2) Very Good (3) Good (4) Fair (5) Unsatisfactory.

Testimonial (To be completed with a view to civil employment and with relation to Certificate of Qualifications and the Job Description)

CPL GARDNER has proved himself to be capable of hard work for long periods without supervision. His work has been of a consistently high standard and has always tried to set a high standard of achieve. He has a serious outlook on life in general but also has a sense of humour. He has many outside interests and has tried to obtain extra educational qualifications. It is unfortunate that he is being discharged on medical grounds as he would have undoubtedly advanced within the Intelligence Corps.

The above assessments have been read to me.

Signature of Soldier
Date 17 MAY 81
Address 35 Falkland St Hyndland Glasgow

Signature of C.O.
Commanding HQ INT & SY GP (UKLF)
DELHI BARRACKS
Unit stamp TIDWORTH. HANTS.
TEL: TIDWORTH MIL 2801

Chapter 3

THE WHITE KNIGHT

'So faithful in love, so dauntless in war,
There never was knight like the young Lochinvar.'

    Walter Scott, *Marmion*, canto v, stanza 12

'Some say the age of chivalry is past, that the spirit of romance is dead. The age of chivalry is never past so long as there is a wrong left unaddressed on earth.'

    Charles Kingsley, *Life*, vol. 2, chapter 28

So how can I describe more about who Colin was? Well, he was someone who saw himself as a white knight, trying to do the right thing. He was flawed, as we all are, but he had an ideal that he aspired to.

Colin loved literature and words – he had quotation books full of beautifully hand written pithy sayings and philosophies of life. It was an enormous notebook, and Colin loved reading and picking out these sayings and poems. He liked to reflect on the nature of goodness and what it means in the world. Some of his favourites included:

'When I was a boy of fourteen, my Father was so ignorant I could hardly stand to have the old man around. But when I got to 21, I was astonished at how much he had learned in seven years.'

    Mark Twain

'For so long as but a hundred of us are left alive, we will in no way yield ourselves to the dominion of the English. For it is not for glory, nor riches nor honour that we fight, but for freedom only, which no good man lays down, but with his life.'

    Declaration of Arbroath 1320

'We are all in the gutter, but some of us are looking at the stars.'

Anonymous

'What passing bells for those who die as cattle?
Only the monstrous anger of the guns.'

Wilfred Owen

'This story is to be neither an accusation or a confession and least of
all an adventure, for death is not an adventure to those who stand
face to face with it. It will try simply to tell of a generation of men
who, even though they escaped its shells, were destroyed by war.'

Erich Maria Remarque, *All Quiet on the Western Front*

These quotations give an insight into Colin's thinking – his love for
Scotland, his sense of humour, his hope for the future, and his deep sense of
anguish at all that is lost in war. Colin had many interests, he loved theatre
and music and films. He enjoyed a wide range of music – from Jethro Tull
(not one of my favourites) to Mary Black, to all forms of classical music.
He loved Judy Collins and Renaissance and Marillion. Songs like 'the
universal soldier' appealed to him. We loved going to see films together,
and Colin could appreciate a 'girl's film' as much as any other – Jane Austen
or even a 'weepie'. Yet his favourite were war films – Salvador, Platoon,
Jacob's ladder, The Heart of Darkness, Full Metal Jacket, The Cruel Sea,
Bridge over the River Kwai, Saving Private Ryan. I watched all these films
with him, as he sought to understand the relationship between war and
life. The brutalisation of war was such a big thing to understand, and I
used to puzzle over it all with him. The impact of watching such films too
often, was a feeling of being exposed to relentless savagery and misery,
which once it was in your mind, was hard to escape from.

One of the memories that Colin often spoke about was being one of the
first on the scene where a car bomb had gone off. He describes arriving on
the scene with his colleagues Graeme and John.

**We drove into a recently built residential area of nice looking semi-
detached houses with gardens and garages. Turning left at the end of
the avenue we could see the scene of the incident just four more houses
ahead. There was already a local uniformed unit there and I could
see smoke rising above the wreckage of the car. The constables were**

involved in keeping people away from the scene. The usual audience mix of those genuinely concerned, the curious and the sensation seekers looking for something they could repeatedly describe for days with pin-point accuracy as to how 'absolutely terrible' the whole thing was. Graeme parked the car up on the pavement to allow access for other services and we all got out. We headed towards the nearest constable whom was already approaching us. We displayed our identification and asked him about the scene.

'They're definitely all dead, it's like a soup inside. That's the mother up there,' he said, pointing towards a young woman standing in a front doorway. She had a completely glazed expression over her face and her hair and clothes were in disarray with small pieces of wreckage from the blast hanging on her. The front windows of the house and most of the neighbours were shattered, with pieces of scrap from the car strewn over the adjacent lawns. The woman just stared fixedly at the wreckage of the car.

'The mother?' John queried.

'Aye, she had two daughters eight and twelve, I think. Her husband was in the R.U.C (part time) Reserve, always took the girls to school before going on to his work. She appeared in the doorway shortly after we arrived. Don't say a thing and don't move. We thought it best to leave her until the Ambulance boys arrived.

'Probably best' John said, studying the woman's expression.

Two land rovers, Army and Police pulled up at the end of the avenue and soldiers and constables climbed out, immediately, setting about the task of putting up accident barriers and moving the audience further back from the scene.

'Any idea of the precise time of the explosion?' Graeme asked the constable.

'Going by the neighbours descriptions, it must have been spot on 08:04,' he replied.

'And both kids were in the car?' John asked

'Aye, sure' he replied.

'Okay, thanks,' Graeme said. 'Colin, you go up and try talk to the woman, see if you can get her to say something. John and I will take an initial look at the car and see if there's any obvious evidence and we'll get you to take some photos after that. But as regards the woman, if you have any success, try and get her to go back into the house and sit down, or something. Get her out of the view of that lot. And see if she'll take a glass of water, or something'.

Nodding, I said: 'Okay, right . . .' and started to move.

Colin wrote about what it was like later on, to go back to the barracks, where sometimes not much was happening, and go over it all again and again in his mind . . .

Everyone in the squad had a room in the barracks but these were only for use during some crises. Apart from the guard force, myself and the other intelligence officers were the only permanent residents. Talk about being lonely? Not that it mattered much, with that pace of life, if you weren't working you'd be eating, sleeping or getting drunk – or some combination of those.

After walking into the barracks, I made myself something resembling a meal in the kitchen and studied the walls and the kitchen fittings whilst I age it. Then with a cup of tea, I moved into the TV room and sat down to a tour of the TV channels whilst I flicked through the stations with one hand and drank my tea with the other. With the conclusion there was nothing worth watching I switched the TV off and poured the remains of my tea down the sink.

I was feeling exhausted as I headed towards my room, but at the same time I was also mentally alert. Ever since Graeme had informed me in the Intelligence Office as to the girl's death, she had been given birth inside my mind and soul. I kept restructuring the events to see if she might still be alive in another version. If I'd gone to the car before approaching the mother; if I'd been more competent or practised with resuscitation might she be alive? Was it kinder that she should die? These kinds of questions, and others, reverberated around my head.

In my room, I locked the door behind me, as per normal security procedure, even though the whole concept of security was little more than a joke. There were insufficient numbers of police constables on permanent duty to cover the area of the Barracks, so we made what amendments we could to help. I took most of my clothes off leaving them to hang on any convenient protrusion and flopped onto the bed. I put my gun under my pillow, switched the light off and stared into the dark oblivion of my surrounding room. With the recurrent possibility of snipers the rooms had to be 'blacked' out so as not to reveal any indication that the rooms were occupied and also, where that person was in the room.

The events of the car bomb continually repeated and restructured themselves inside me. Grating like a pointed steel, chain belt, inside a delicate crystal format. The girl's first soft questioning sigh; a pleading puzzled note from a voice of gentle unaccusing innocence. The last refugee in the holocaust of obliterated beauty, a sigh that had become an accusing, scream of guilt.

I rolled and twisted from one part of the bed to another. I was so tired, yet couldn't find sufficient mental calm in order to fall asleep. I switched the light on and stared at the bleak sparse furnishings of the room, then turned if off again. I pushed the covers back as I got hotter, although with the light on, I could see my breath.

I fought with my thoughts trying to control them but continually losing. I bit the knuckle of my hand in an attempt to break the pattern via pain. That failed, and I tried again, and that failed.

At times all I could do was weep with him – the poignance of senseless obliteration, cruelty and darkness. I began to feel that I had been all these places too, and that was a constant danger for my soul. It could be an overwhelming darkness always present in the shadows, threatening to overwhelm our lives, and to snuff out any sense of hope. Other films absorbed Colin too – Lawrence of Arabia, El Cid, Ben Hur – the nobility of true men of integrity in battle. These films helped to balance out some of the misery and pain. And Colin saw himself in this light – the white knight – going out into the battlefield to do good, to work for justice and truth.

This romantic ideal of the heroic knight was a key theme in Colin – a necessary corollary to the memories that disturbed him – and some of these accounts of his memories are in his writings. In order to cope with the injustices that he remembered, the pain of the screams of war, he needed to interpret it in a philosophical framework which made sense. He needed to know that his decisions and actions mattered, and weren't just lost in oblivion. Yet there was also another dimensions to Colin's keen sense of justice, his faith and hope for the future, and these themes were also strong. To gain insight again into Colin's way of thinking, I include some quotes from Colin himself:

'Some think that by 25 they should at least be close to marriage, the beginning of a family, helping to contribute to life and the society around them.

By 25, I'd killed people, wrecked lives, and was a war pensioner.

At 30, because of my military injuries, I'd died.'

'Throughout my life, however short it may be, I must stick to my principles and ideals for they are what makes me a man. I must not bow down, or allow myself to be manipulated for the sake of expediency or reward, for in the long run I would be miserable. We are all just men, and no-one has the right to control another's life. All are indeed created equal and remain so whatever the circumstances.

A man can only be commanded by consent.

When I die, I must be able to look back and see that I have lived my life.'

On time in N Ireland:

'With ideals a man must be an island, free from external indifference . . . So that ideals might be kept pure in order for them to be put to the betterment of his fellow men and the preservation of his freedom. For it is only by the preservation of your fellow man's freedom and liberty, have you any chance of preserving your own.'

CSG 1977 NI

'I cannot blindly follow orders for I am ultimately responsible for the consequences of my actions. Nor can I be blind to the actions of others. I must always question, question, question my superiors, my colleagues, for I am just as guilty of any crime against my fellow man as the instigator, if I stand by and do nothing.'

'Memories are the sum total of our lives as we now are. Yet without the conscious intelligence to be aware of these memories, use their collective experiences to cope with our present, to anticipate and prepare for our possible futures, we are less than animals. We become uncoordinated reactions to the moment, incapable of even developing instinct.'

5/12/89

That was written after a period of time when Colin felt his mind was slowly losing its power to think and reason . . . earlier he wrote many poems, like:

ETERNAL SUNRISE

The orange lash on an eternal green dawn,
unveils broken, slate grey prospects.
Wet with insipid rain of widows tears,
that light more candles, to another's God.

Sins of loyal isolation, celebrated in communion,
seek Sunday's forgiveness, for those yet to come.
The promise of annual parade, bright colours pass by in time,
to justify in sight of God, another cross on a graveyard line.

Born with life to live, raised of parental hate,
to practise malice, prior to learning the date.
Remorseless memory, foul with insensate repetition,
preserving ghosts, to stain the seed of daily intercourse.

Monotonous blood red colours, paint another's portrait,
A different model, an organised still life.
The blindfolded seek for light in a bottomless pit,
oiled with the slime of religious right.

The exhausting rain of tragedy's tears,
wash the blood of wounds, which refuse to heal.
Yesterday's colourless birthright, a future long gone,
the orange lash, of an eternal green dawn.

After building our relationship up over many years, we decided to get married. We prayed, and it seemed the right thing to do. We had been engaged only a couple of days, when my dad died – he had been suffering from lung cancer for some months. We didn't publicise the engagement till the beginning of the next year. We planned the wedding and started to work out whom to invite. It was an exciting time of hope. Both families were very supportive.

Colin moved into a new flat – a bigger flat with more room. We started to think of how things might develop in the future. We talked of the wedding service, the reception, the honeymoon. There was lots to plan and to do, and only 6 months in which to do it! It all worked out in the end, with some interesting moments along the way. It was a new start, a second life, which we felt blessed to have.

OUR WEDDING

I am your land
Wherever you step, I shall support you.

I am your land
Whatever you need, I shall provide.

I am your land
When you are tired, lie down and sleep with me.

I am your land
Join with me and let us harvest together.

I am your land
Let me blossom with you, from year to year.

I am your land
Storms may hurt us, but let us recover together.

I am your land
When we have sunshine, let us dance together.

I am your land
Let us share each other, mutual dependency for life.

I am your land
End time with me, secure in the re-birth of life.

1999

Colin wrote poems about love and new beginnings: he anticipated a better life to come. He wrote the following poems about love and security and healing. I include these, because they tell more about Colin's identity, and his depth of feeling.

TO A PHOTOGRAPH

Young woman standing, by a riverside,
surrounded by a world, which waits on you.
Numerous stones lie arranged, with single mind,
for chance the prize, of a touch by you.

Young woman encircled, by rich green trees,
crowding the riverside, queuing for sight of you.
Singing silver songs of welcome, the watching river flow
rocks break the surface for a fleeting glimpse of you.

Young woman supporting, the mainstay of life,
for a world set in layers, around you.
The stony ground, seeking water for growth,
lets trees stroke a sky, needing sunlight from you.

Young woman unmoving, time's moment held in a frame,
though each day I gaze, none will change, except you.
The gentle wind brushes through your fine soft hair,
then sighs its secret, throughout all the air.

Young woman giving all, to this still world,
dare I dream you look, in invitation to me?

C.S. Gardner December 1990

A WALTZ

Take my hand tonight, hold it with your own,
pass to me your warm soft silken glow.
Touch me in your tender way, reassure my fear,
chase the pain within away, let me know you're here.

As we sit in close embrace, secure in one another,
holding on with all our strength, floating with each other
Take my hand and lead me, in the tune of our own air
I know I cannot dance alone, the waltz of the millionaire.

Take my fingers into your hair, let them wander through,
allow me to caress and stroke such softness, I never knew.
I breath within your perfect scent, see colours rich and fair
*   although such moments still too rare,*
*   around the fine threads of your hair.*

Take my hand tonight, search a starlit sky with me,
where we go is up to us, from time's account we're free.
Unlock all your inner thoughts, reveal the heart within,
safe inside our sanctuary, souls can pray and sing.

Wash me with the flowing oceans of your living eyes,
share with me the sought for flicker, that others must deny,
Take my hand my love, for I tremble when alone,
then at last I may take yours, and hold it with my own.

C.S. Gardner December 1990 (amended)

A MAN'S FIRST TIME IN SPACE

I looked into your eyes and slipped out into space,
galaxies of stars, a universe within your face.
From this first birth of life, to the beginning of all time,
your smile reveals the joy I can find in sunshine.

A movement of elegance that suggests a dance,
love in eternal spin, life for a romance.
A love only of hope, which only lives in beauty,
such is only found in life, and in you.

Your lips' sweet taste, a gift of melon,
to one as I, who dies from thirst.
There are no silks to test against your skin;
from all the worlds, of all the stars; your skin shall surely win.

Your voice has form and flow so real,
envelops me in presence I can feel.
Sound which invigorates, locks each breath in time,
holds all I wish or need, enshrined in rhyme.

I never knew such beauty 'till I gazed within you,
never knew such purity, in birth of love for two.
Now it's all around me, I'm floating on a sea,
life in a heart, beating for the first time in me.

You've turned me upside down, and back to front,
from left to right and around and about.
I'm floating in space, there's no gravity, no more him,
I can only think of you; prepare for a permanent spin.

C.S. Gardner July 98

25

THE HARBOUR

When trouble's storms throw ships about,
then turn and sail to me.
In dark my lights will lead you,
in fog my voice will guide you.

Enter my harbour, the comfort for this night.
Make safe your ship, leave raging seas outside.

Dry yourself of problem's sprays, from my cup drink deep.
Let warmth turn chill to flow, both inside and out.

Come and clothe yourself in night's soft gentle covers.
Dance each dream secure, only who dare to touch may see.

Lie down you weary traveller, hear my heart's soft music.
Sing the lullaby of yesterday, recover for the dawn.

Then when the storm is over, and you must sail again,
Wave farewell the harbour, never watch it fade away.

Let last night's embrace, forever sail with you.
This harbour for your need, will be forever here.

C.S. Gardner

Chapter 4

THE VOLCANO

'I have often thought that the best way to define a man's character would be to seek out the particular mental or moral attitude in which, when it came upon him, he felt himself deeply and intensively active and alive. At such moments there is a voice inside which speaks and says, "This is the real me".'

William James

'I do not understand what I do. For what I want to do I do not do, but what I hate I do.'

The apostle Paul – Romans 7:15

On the outside, everything looked good – Colin was seeking to be fully himself. But on the inside, Colin was struggling, dealing with his own memories and guilt, which haunted him. Some of these experiences are described at the beginning of this writing, to give a flavour of what he was trying to cope with. Despite his best efforts, enormous willpower and earnest prayer, Colin could not contain the painful traumas he had endured, and that he lived with every day.

Colin often spoke about the incident where he was called to the scene of a car bomb which had exploded, and he had to try to resuscitate one of the children, and to knock at the door of the house to tell the wife and mum what had happened. He would tell the account of this story over and over again. As we read earlier, he remembered this in the barrack room late at night. A kiss should be a sign of love, yet the resuscitation failed, and it just became part of the pattern of meaningless deaths.

THE KISS

The haunting taste,
of recurring dreams.
Of man's addiction,
his hobby, filth.
My private nightmare,
someone's termination.
The hell of hells,
so eternal.

What minds have they,
this damnable filth.
That perpetrate acts,
know in advance, the end.

No minds, no conscience,
Bombs are not politics.
They just kill,
go bang and maim,
Damn this filth.

It's not from any book.
These are not ideals.
This is so real.
Filth for damnation.

A copper, his two kids,
Blown to bits.
The terrorists'
early morning . . . kiss.

Three lumps smouldering,
heaps of soup in scrap metal.
One of the two refuses to leave,
lies with the others sighing.
Then loudly dies, inside my mind.
Three bags more, more for the morgue.

As heart hot tears,
run scalding my face.
Another requiem for uninvited ends.
Will one weep for them, except me?
Do none feel death, but to themselves?

C.S. Gardner

A Shooting Incident in the 1970s

Another incident that he never came to terms with, despite counselling and prayer and reflection, was a time when he was chasing a man who was thought to be armed, and when the man looked as if he was brandishing a gun out of his pocket, Colin fired, as indeed he was trained to do. That split second decision haunted him for the rest of his life.

Colin was pursuing a terrorist suspect. After he shouted out a warning not to move, the young man – about his own age – moved suddenly and unexpectedly, putting his hand inside his jacket, which looked as if he was about to pull out a gun. In that split second Colin had to make a decision, and he shot him.

Although Colin had followed procedure, afterwards, when he realised that the young man was just about his own age, Colin was wracked with remorse and a guilt which never left him. He wrote a poem afterwards, about that guilt which he wrestled with for the rest of his life (on the next page).

THE GAME

Feet hit the ground at alternate rates,
Propel a body on; faster in a race, the deadliest chase.
All to win, or lose, no second chance, no debate.
For glory and honour, if one knew what it was,
or a pine box deep, in the sin-sodden ground.

Lungs drawing in, as my adrenaline flows,
A possible target, thoughts question my actions.
I've never met him, but I'm determined I'll get him,
my hand carries the metal too, that stops a game.

Moving as a wild stream train, white clouds fill a deep, dark, night,
locked within a route; knowing its end; before I can see the destination.
Cold air breathing in, steadies my hand, giving line of sight.
Fears promoting hates, sympathy, succours love,
striving to stay upright, I am inverted, insane, piece of world.

What to do? Who's right? What if he gets away ?
Shout a final cry hate him yet love him; measure him.
Finger contracts, gun explodes, he's knocked head over foot into a
*   wall,*
kicked by the gigantic boot, he lies contorted in pain,
crying about his life's fall.

Shout another warning, pray he'll obey,
move steady with caution, gun leading the way.
Pleading, 'don't be stupid', I sweat inside,
ready, on a smile, to end a life.

Very close, it's going to be okay, just keep lying there; but suddenly;
he twists, pulling his hand, and something out.
I squeeze. Head exploding, his body leaps.
No time to shout, sliding down his blood upon a wall, eyes follow me.
Staring in accusation for what I did to him, a life no more to be.

Swearing at him, I try to turn the guilt of conscience back around,
It's all your fault, I'd told you what; playing a stupid game; nothing
    won,
Staring back at him, I try to estimate his age,
seventeen or eighteen ? Maybe more, maybe less.

I collect myself, start to check him over,
anything of interest, I feel back in control.
Surprised I so easily regained myself, I guess that's why I'm in this job.
Admit there may be problems later, I'm sure, I'll be alright.
At this time, I have no idea' of the mental bomb still to detonate.

C.S. GARDNER

Incidents like these replayed themselves inside Colin's mind again and again, and made him question just what it was all about. A relentless flood of such incidents, filled him with rage and questioning and fury. That raw questioning is demonstrated in the following two poems. The first is about the death of a friend.

A TICKET FOR THE SHOW

You posthumously made page four,
Terminated, knocking on someone else's door.
You were must a corpse in the front row,
Of a political, religious horror show.

50 pence a day, free for all !
Welcome one, welcome all !
Roll up, fall down
See life's horror show.

Why did you join, become a soldier,
A dying trade, of patriotic suicide?
You were maybe tired of endless interviews,
The never ending weekly giro queue.

50 pence a day, free for all!
Welcome to you, welcome all!
Roll up, fall apart.
See life's horror show.

You in eggshell uniform, the soldier's grasp at price,
Trading all as I crawled into mine.
You shall not see the twilight of your day,
As I and others shall may yet see ours.

50 pence a day, free tickets!
Welcome to him, welcome to me!
Roll away, fall and to
See life's endless horror show.

Death was no answer, but it . . .
Thrilled, excited, frightened and soothed.
Death robbed you honestly, with equality,
Simplicity with no duplicity.

50 pence a day, cheap for all!
Welcome to them, welcome to us!
Roll up, Roll up
See life's horror show.

And when your world exploded in a rubbish bin,
There was no Seventh Cavalry, no sign of John Wayne.
As you paced the streets, leapt from door to door,
the reassuring feel of a rifle grip,
we're nervous of a noise, wary of a pram,
weary of what long ceased to be a game.

50 pence a day, free for free !
Just sign on the dotted line, please,
This door Sir, no this one,
See life's horror show.

You could not see, as we shovelled you up,
Tossing your bits, on a black tarpaulin sheet.
You 'were' honourably mentioned, on page four,
But tomorrow, you'll be garbage
Another body bag, a refuse bag.

C. S. Gardner August 1989 (from notes 1975)

FORGOTTEN SONS

Armalite, street lights, night sights.
Searching the roofs for a sniper, viper, fighter.
Death in the shadows he'll maim you, wound you, kill you
for a long forgotten cause, on not so foreign shores,
*   boys baptised in wars.*

Morphine, chill scream, bad dream.
Serving as numbers on dogtags, flakrags, sandbags.
Your girl has married your best friend, loves end, poison pen.
Your flesh will always creep, tossing turning sleep,
*   the wounds that burn so deep.*

Your mother sits at the edge of the world
*   when the cameras start to roll.*
Panoramic viewpoints resurrect the killing fold.
Your father drains another beer he's one of the few that cares,
crawling behind a Saracen's hull from the safety of his living room
*   chair.*
Forgotten Sons, Forgotten Sons, Forgotten Sons.

And so as I patrol in the valley of the shadow of the Tricolor
I must fear evil, for I am but mortal and mortals can only die.
Asking questions, pleasing answers, from the nameless
*   faceless watchers*
that stalk the carpeted corridors of Whitehall,
who order desecration, mutilation, verbal masturbation
in their guarded bureaucratic wombs.

Minister, Minister, care for your children,
order then not into damnation,
to eliminate those who would trespass against you,
for whose is the Kingdom the power and the glory,
forever and ever AAAAAAmen – Halt, Who Goes There ?
    DEATH – Approach friend.

You're just another coffin on its way down the emerald aisle,
where the children's stony glances
mourn your death in a terrorist's smile,
the Bomber's arm places fiery gifts on the supermarket shelves,
alleys sing with shapnel, detonate a temporary hell, Forgotten Sons.

From the dole queue to the regiment, a profession in a flash,
but remember Monday signings when from door to door you dash,
on the news a nation mourns you, unknown soldier count the cost,
for a second you'll be famous but labelled posthumous.

Forgotten Sons, Forgotten Sons
peace on earth and mercy mild,
Mother Brown has lost her child,
just another Forgotten Son.

                                          C.S. Gardner 1980

These poems speak to the enormous pain and anguish of soul that Colin wrestled with, and which explained the volcanic eruptions that could come at any time. So many things could take him back into this dark world, a world of violence and hatred and sorrow. He wondered who he was. At one stage he looked in a mirror – he saw both a young man looking back, and an old man whose eyes reflected the experiences that had made him old before his time.

THE MIRROR

A man just in life, stood at the mirror, looking to each eye,
started to run and jump, taking each and every lie.
As the race progressed, paused, did he want this,
was he just endorsing a previous generation's wish?
Lay there some other, undiscovered field,
for his unsown harvest there to yield?

Then acting on an impulse, he signed away his life,
'Want to be a mighty man, never fear the knife.'
Professions birth of majesty, born for a written name;
naive and young, still playing a film and T.V. game.
The education of a blinkered vision, to what is really done,
to things unseen and sights not there, education for the son.

Words so wide and deep, so full of monstrous freaks,
political hell and legal lies, tied up filth that reeks.
The scars of life, the tears for death, intoxications fear,
no more love, the missing value, the loss of what was dear.
The hand too burnt by reaching for the golden apple tree.
But now he has vision, self decision, now he can see.

And what now of the scores he witnessed, discarded to the side,
those he helped nudge and trip, from those he'll never hide.
The nag of guilt, a penitential bite, for this horrendous loss;
their priceless value, his I.D. tags of trade, life at cheap cost.
A man looks in the morrow now, studying himself so cold.
Does he see an old man young, or a young man old?

C.S. Gardner (July 89 from notes C.1984)

Chapter 5

NEW BEGINNINGS, DARK SHADOWS

'Never underestimate yourself or what God can do in your life because remember, it was professionals who built the Titanic, but amateurs who built the ark.'

Anonymous

'The light at the end of the tunnel could be an on-coming train.'

A favourite quote of Colin's!

In time, as we progressed further into our marriage, I started to notice that now and again Colin could get intensely angry about little things. In a certain mood, anything that he took to be a 'slight' against him personally, could precipitate him into a rage. It was like an adrenalin high, that he needed to express this tremendous pain inside. Sometimes he would go off into the night, and walk for hours in the rain, just to try and get rid of this enormous anguish and rage he was feeling. He often talked about his stories from the military – about the horror that he felt over certain incidents. He seemed to go over them again and again in his mind.

I went and spoke to a former army chaplain, who recommended that Colin be assessed for post-traumatic stress (PTSD).*[1] There were a number of signs of Colin reacting to events as a result of what he had been through – e.g. round about the 5th of November was a bad time for us, because of the noise of the fireworks. When a firework went off near Colin, he would often jump or fall to the floor, thinking it was a bullet or a bomb. He would be so startled and upset and fearful. One time he was outside putting the rubbish out, and the noise started him so much that he fell over and broke his ankle, and needed a metal plate put in afterwards.

---

* An asterisk followed by a number indicates a reference to the Glossary of Medical Terms at the back of the book (Appendix 2).

Colin's love for watching old war movies also was a mixed blessing, as he would watch *The Cruel Sea,* or later on *Saving Private Ryan* repeatedly, which did nothing for his mood! He would go through periods where all he could do was to bleakly relive trauma again and again. It was as if much of his identity was in the past – 'I was a war hero' . . . 'I served in the intelligence services' . . . 'I once was a valued and purposeful person' . . . and these were the only places he could feel alive and find solace.

And so we went down to the nearest military Garrison over a period of months in 1997. Colin wrote about a dream he had before he went to Catterick:

My own ending is my own end, to start is to finish. Time-loop – eternity. Each end is completely different. Everything has an opposite. But as each end pulls further away from the other, each gets closer to the other. At some point in the middle, as at the end and the beginning, one will finish as the other starts.

At some point on the highway, I shall crash into the rear of a car, as a car shall crash into my rear.

I will become more knowledgeable, as I become more stupid.

If I flew round the earth the opposite to how it revolves would I see sunset before sunrise?

Become more perfect as I become imperfect?

Recognise beauty as I inevitably witness horror?

Become beautiful as I become more ugly?

Feel pain as I feel more peace?

Feel hate more intensely as I feel love more deeply?

Move faster as I move more slowly?

At any one point in time you can have a present and a past but never a future. There are always so many different possibilities for the future it can never be predicted, except at the one point where I possess all knowledge, understanding and will know everything about my life and beyond it, where I will know that I must start again in order to reach my point of culmination. And how to start.

The bubble of thoughts in the ambulance experience. A three dimensional bubble shrinking before me as I was also inside it, aware that it was closing on me from all points at the same time, yet I was not in the least frightened, because I seemed to know that it was inevitable to end in order to begin again.

Fear is the forced change of conditions that one feels inadequate to prevent. Fear was an unknown quantity. I couldn't feel it. I didn't know such a feeling existed, yet I was not 100% sure that when the bubble finally closed, I would begin again. I also thought it was possible that on closure everything for me would be over. But still no evidence of fear. Which is not a sudden influx of courage, just the total awareness of one's complete powerlessness to act.

Like a cross where different lines travel towards each other in order to meet and become their own beginning because they are only one at the start. The lines will multiply without a final quantity as they will become all things at all times. And as all things exist at all times, not all things can exist at all times, but only at some times. Hence at any one part of time you have a present and a past but an undecided future. The 3-d bubble expanding and contracting like a breathing of life.

If I am to become all things at all times, do I then become one, become God, as only he could have the capacity to think all thoughts at all times at once. I, Colin Gardner, am one thought with a present and a past and unlimited futures. This as I write, is me advancing into this particular one. I am one thought within my own mind, forever advancing, as with all my thoughts to my own culmination and beginning. Each is necessary for the other to exist. As I approach all thoughts, I shall start myself at the most basic part – e.g. an atom/electron/proton/neutron.

Eternity – everything is in existence at all times, although at any one time only one thing or thought is aware of its own existence. Although one thought will constantly be meeting different parts of itself as I meet different people on the earth and live different days one after the other. The universe as I see the stars at night is one area that I have yet to encounter – the future. Although each universe contains an infinite number of universes within itself, so it also is an infinite number of universes as it also is within one part of another universe. Everything can be smaller as it can be larger – a universe within an atom. No limit to size, more or less in the dream, aware of living the same scene an infinite number of times, but each time a little more than before, each are identical but each are different from the one before and the one after. The mental coherence / consciousness is exciting as it is frightening. Trapped inside yourself, the only way out is your own end and beginning.

Are these thoughts a result of a day trip to Catterick, stress, the effects of medication, the effects of counselling, worse before it gets better, opening up wounds, relating to Holy Week?'

Another dream at this time:

I am fighting invisible ghosts with chairs or any available furniture. The ghosts are hurting and killing people, and I eventually stand before them with the cross of Christ. Before the name of Jesus, they materialise to scare me off, and I force them away. (I do lots of kicking and punching in the bed.)

They interviewed Colin over a period of time to assess for PTSD, and in addition took Colin for a two week assessment, and they wrote a report which concluded:

'Mr Gardner is not suffering from post-traumatic stress disorder.

We believe that he is suffering from an organic personality disorder,[*2] secondary to head injuries sustained in the military and is at a very high risk of developing a depressive episode.'

This description puzzled me for many years, as I couldn't understand how head injuries had led to an organic personality disorder, but I have concluded that this was just another way to avoid saying 'PTSD'.

On the long drive back from one of these visits from Catterick to Glasgow, Colin became very down in the car on the way back, and at a garage we stopped at for petrol, he became agitated and decided to run away into the fields. I think he felt helpless and worried that he had a life sentence of struggle and guilt to cope with, with not much to relieve it.

It was dark – about 11pm and pouring with rain. Colin verbalised his discontent – a thing he was always very good at. He wanted me to come and find him, and to give him reasons to live. Slithering about in muddy puddles in the middle of a field out in the middle of nowhere, trying to find Colin and then encourage him to be hopeful for the future was a dire experience. Eventually he agreed to get back in the car. It took me a while to realise that I was not responsible for Colin's decisions – all I could do was be loving and consistent, but at times it was such very wearisome work.

In many ways we were no further forward. Already Colin did receive a small military pension for his epilepsy, and that seemed the only recognition that he was going to get. The doctors had decided that they would not give him a PTSD diagnosis. Over the years, I did on occasion appeal for Colin's disability pension to increase, through form filling and descriptions of his abilities and interviews. These assessments were often belittling and depressing, and hard to contemplate, never mind engage with. Doctors would visit the house to do an assessment, and say things like the date on this packet of medication is not the right chronological date, because I didn't always use the packets of medications in the order I was given them from the chemist. However for the visiting doctor, this was apparently highly suspicious, and cast doubt on our honesty and the true nature of Colin's condition.

Colin was still often unhappy. He could survive for long periods of time, friendly, considerate and generous in spirit – his true nature. He kept going to church and loved singing in the choir, listening to the sermons, puzzling over the philosophical nature of it all. Yet there were other times when he was sad and moody. His epilepsy became slightly less well controlled. Colin's GP suggested that his anti-convulsant medication come down as it was in danger of being toxic. The drug he was on was called phenytoin.[*3] Yet when the level of medication came down, after a day or two Colin would become disorientated and aggressive – it seemed to have an enormous effect upon him. He would pace up and down, agitated and feeling as if he was going to die. Sometimes it seemed to cause sensory overload – he would feel as if there was water running over his skin all the time, or as if he was underwater. And so after a week or so, the medication would be put back up, and different 'in between' levels would be tried to see if it were possible to get better seizure control. Colin was having about two seizures a month – in his sleep.

Sometimes he couldn't go into work the next day, as sleep seemed the best thing to help him recover, and he would sleep till 1pm in the afternoon. The GP suggested introducing a second anti-convulsant – neurontin.[*4] At the beginning this seemed to make a bit of a difference, but over time it became harder to work out if it was really helping. The attempts at medication changes made it hard for Colin, as there were times when he needed time off work. We went to see a consultant, who suggested that Colin's phenytoin level needed to be brought down. When we explained the effects that Colin went through when his levels were decreased, she then said that she had never heard of anything like this, and that she thought that Colin must be psychologically dependent on this drug, and that this drug must still be changed. Our consultant said that reducing the phenytoin was the best solution for Colin, and that we would be behaving unethically if we did not follow this path, and that if we insisted on not doing this, that she would have to refer us to another consultant. She seemed enraged that we had a different opinion from her, and she said she would deal with us no longer.

We reached a mutual agreement that it would be better for us to see someone else. Trying to keep Colin as well as possible seemed the most important option, and taking the phenytoin down meant going through these horrific side effects and then having poorer seizure control. That didn't seem like a real choice. We felt that Colin had to stay on the same level of phenytoin, as he had a reasonable quality of life, and every time when we had tried to change it, it had been disastrous. We were therefore referred to a different consultant in the same hospital. We went through the same conversations, but this time Colin was a referred to a neuro psychologist to see if he had a psychological dependence on phenytoin.

Over a series of appointments, she really listened to Colin, and it seemed to be recognised that Colin could remain on that level of phenytoin, although he would have to be checked regularly for signs of toxicity. We were pleased with this, because this seemed to give Colin the best quality of life at this time. The minutiae of these changes are related because such small changes had such a big effect on our lives. Chronic illness involves an endless round of appointments and medication changes and reviews, that they eventually become all that there is. We all end up talking incessantly about appointments – how long we waited for the appointment, how long we were in the waiting room, the attitude of the nurse, the chat we overheard and what it might mean, analysing the body language of the nurses, what the doctor said and didn't say. However at this point, we were just glad to be listened to, and for Colin to have some respite.

Over the next few years, we had a reasonable quality of life. We travelled – we went on holiday to Russia, where we visited Moscow after a snow fall, and saw the capital city looking proudly and magnificently Slavic in her sparkly beauty. We travelled overnight on the train to St Petersburg, and visited the Summer and Winter palaces and Dostoevsky's house. We saw ballets and concerts and cathedrals and art galleries. Colin as always, was brilliant at not conforming – in Moscow he was always last in the tour group, proudly wearing his furry Russian hat, stopping to examine whatever interested him, oblivious of the group having moved on long ago, and obviously, the one most likely to inadvertently set off any alarm in the highly security conscious museums. He loved too being stopped at the airport in Moscow, because of the metal implant in his ankle setting of the metal detector. Our Russian language did not stretch to explaining this to the very stern and unamused guard. Colin thought this was exciting!

We went to Paris on the Eurostar, and almost missed it. We ran along the platform just before the doors closed, and landed on the train in a heap. We saw the sights, we went up the Eiffel Tower and went for quiet meals. We lived, and it was wonderful. Life could be good, unless interrupted suddenly by seizures or black moods, but we learned to live in the moment.

And best of all, we were blessed with a beautiful baby boy. Andrew was born, and he was amazing! Colin was at the birth, and it was a great time – a time of rejoicing and thanksgiving and tears – such a proud moment for Colin to drive us both home from the hospital, Andrew in his car seat just three days old! He had just been given some oral antibiotics (Andrew that is – not Colin!), and he blew pink bubbles all the way home. The first weeks and months were chaotic – but good. Colin was a good dad, even changing nappies! And he was so very happy to have a son.

During this time, there was another underlying theme, very quietly gaining momentum. The doctors were still tweaking Colin's medication now and again, and this caused him to have time off work. A few times he was brought home from work, unable to function after a seizure. His mood became more erratic – sometimes he could get quite irritable with people. An incident at work brought matters to a head – and the occupational health consultants offered Colin early retirement on medical grounds. We hesitated – Colin had so much more to give. Yet he was putting enormous stress on himself trying to conform to all the regulations and requirements of his job. And so we accepted, and Colin became a house husband.

When Andrew was a few months old, the doctors suggested Colin try a different anti-convulsant – lamotrogine.[*5] Foolishly we decided to try this. However we were not to know that Colin's mood was to change on this drug. He used to have what was described as 'bright dreams'. These dreams were very intense – to use the 60's words psychedelic, multi-coloured.

43

Colin always dreams in three dimensions, very vivid and captivating. Sometimes he could control his dreams, and choose what would happen next – he could fly or visit places he wanted to be. These dreams on this new medication were even more intense – so much so that he didn't want to wake up. He just wanted to stay there for ever. He could orchestrate his dreams as he wished – he could go to particular places, even to fly and he would not want to get up in the morning.

This made real life feel really hollow and superficial for him, he was so captivated, entranced, enthralled by his dreams. One day, not wanting to stay in this life any longer, he decided to end it all, and he slit his wrist. We had to go the local Accident and Emergency in the car – one bleeding husband and a small baby. The staff were so lovely, but it all seemed surreal. Imagine trying to nurture a small baby and welcome new life into the world, whilst also to have to help a grown up to see why he should want to remain in the real world just a bit longer.

It was heart wrenching – it wasn't that Colin didn't love us, but just that his medication and its effects were so intense that everything else became completely diluted in meaning.

Shortly afterwards, Colin was taken off this medication. In hindsight, it was not very holistic thinking to try Colin on a new medicine at this vulnerable time in our lives. We should have said, no we will not try this till our own lives were more settled. Going through these events, I just had to take them in my stride, but there was often an emotional backlash, as I tried to take on board what had happened. A very small part of me was angry that Colin would have done such a thing, but another part of me had seen him suffer so much, that I could understand that at times living life just seemed too difficult.

Eventually, at one of the routine hospital visits, our consultant said that he was concerned about Colin's reflexes and that he needed a nerve conductivity test. This confirmed the consultant's fears – the phenytoin had caused a peripheral neuropathy in Colin's feet which was rising upwards, and which would eventually cause him to be paralysed. The only alternative was to take him off this drug completely. We were told that the neuropathy would travel quickly, and that we did not have a lot of time. The damage done already should be reversible, but might not be.

We decided that we did not really have a choice – we needed to have a change of drug. (As I write this, I am conscious that I keep saying 'we' and I know that I was not physically on any of these drugs – the treatment was for Colin. Yet the consequences were so major for me as his wife, it seemed as if we were joined in these matters!) I was really concerned that this change of medication should not take place at home, as it was such a drastic change with unpredictable effects, and the consultant arranged for the drug change to happen at Quarriers Epilepsy centre at Bridge of Weir. Colin was to have a six week placement there as an in patient. Meantime, he was on neurontin and phenytoin at this time. A tertiary drug was brought in, trileptal,[*6] and Colin was started on this. He was to enter Quarriers[*7] around March 2001.

When I took Colin to Quarriers, it was with mixed feelings. I wanted him to be well, so I wanted a new medication to be effective – yet I wasn't sure what such a change would entail. Colin was no longer working, but he had many interests in life. I took Colin to Quarriers with his bag packed and with his books. He had just started a University evening class in philosophy. He went out jogging now and again. He was interested in politics and chess and had these books with him. He was allowed out of Quarriers if I went to visit. I went along, and we went out for a curry one evening. We went for a curry in a wee restaurant in Bridge of Weir. It was a lovely evening – Colin was in good form, benevolent in mood, lively and interactive with lots of stories and thoughts. I took him back to his ward and then drove home. All the way home in the car I cried, as I wondered if I would ever see Colin like this again? I had no particular reason to think like this, but my instinct was that we were entering uncertain territory, and it was terrifying.

The medication started to change. The new medication went up to a more therapeutic[*8] level. Colin was a bit sluggish, a bit unsure. His seizure rate remained stable however. Things seemed to be going quite well. I took Andrew to visit his dad – he was one and a half years old, and he mourned his dad's loss round the house in his own way. He couldn't articulate it in words, so he became very clingy. Photos of the time show him usually with me or his teddy! I think we were interchangeable! Understandably, Andrew was so confused as to what was happening. On one fateful evening at Quarriers, Colin got into the car for a chat when we were about to leave. When he got out, Andrew started howling – he had thought his dad was going to come back with him! He was very upset all the way home.

The phenytoin medication started to come down. Everything seemed to be going well in the first couple of weeks. I thought that our fears had been needless – everything seemed fine. And then it started. I visited – and Colin seemed agitated. He felt that there were strange sensation in his limbs. He was disconcerted by the strange messages he felt his limbs were giving him. He felt his sight and hearing weren't quite right – it was if he was under water. He became irritable and unsettled. As usual, I felt pretty powerless. I was watching him suffer even more. The staff gave him temazepam*[9] and haloperidol*[10] to settle him and relieve his symptoms. They expressed their concerns to me that I should ask him to be more compliant, as he was becoming aggressive. I wondered how I was expected to do this.

On one day I thought I would take him out to the cinema to provide a distraction. It was a May day, and it was very hot. Colin seemed quite subdued when I got to the ward, but we went out just the same. We had a long drive in the car and there was a traffic jam – it was a sticky, long day. When we got to the cinema complex and we had some lunch, Colin was very slow. He ate his dinner with his fingers, I realised with a start, that he had no idea what he was meant to do with his knife and fork. He was relying on his basic instincts – so fingers it was.

As we went across to the cinema, a very small distance, he had to walk really slowly and was unsteady. I got the tickets and the ice cream. We entered the cinema, and a cry came up from Colin: 'I can't see!' Immediately my mind thought – what is the medication doing now, what could be wrong, he seems to be going blind. I looked at him in consternation, when I noticed that he still had his shades on! No wonder he couldn't see anything – his sunglasses and a dark cinema were not a good combination. We took the sunglasses off, and he watched the film. I don't think he understood anything of the film and his eyes kept shutting. When we eventually got back to Colin's ward, I said I felt he was not functioning well, and they told me that he had been a bit agitated that morning, and they had given him some haloperidol. I wish they had told me before we had left!

Colin's six week stay became 11 weeks. The trileptal did not seem to be seem to be working very well, so this drug was brought down, and a new drug, keppra,*[11] was introduced. Keppra was introduced as a great new wonder drug. Colin was having quite a few seizures during this process. He continued to have bouts of anger and irritability. At one point the consultant told me that if I couldn't persuade Colin to behave better, then they would send him home. They had him interviewed by a psychiatrist to see if he was psychotic.*[12] The psychiatrist said he was not mentally ill, but he was having a psychotic episode (defined as interpreting things differently from those around him: e.g. through hallucinations and/or delusions).

I was present when another consultant very compassionately told Colin to stop getting so upset and angry as he had so much to live for. Yet as I listened to this, and looked at Colin, I felt that he really barely understood what they were saying, never mind how to respond to it. It felt unrealistic for a consultant to expect Colin to respond to a reasoned argument, as he was barely coping with reality at all. It seemed he was so drugged that he was not in control of his own mind. After another couple of weeks, the keppra level was up and stable, and Colin was back to about a seizure a week. He seemed well enough to be discharged, and he was discharged about the middle of June.

We had booked a holiday for July down at the lake district, and so we went on holiday. When Colin got out of Quarriers, he was very subdued and slept a lot. At times he seemed a bit distant. I thought that his body had been through a complicated series of changes of drugs and medication, and that it would take him a long time to recover. Colin slept till lunch time most days. He had 3 seizures in two weeks. He was sluggish and at times disorientated. Andrew was almost two years old, and he got up enthusiastically at 6am every morning. Colin by contrast was usually not up till 12 noon. Andrew was going down about 7pm, and Colin was up till midnight. I felt as if I was caught between their two different time zones and worlds. There was only a brief time of overlap, and trying to spend time with both of them, I never really felt fully awake. Colin seemed a bit dazed by all that had happened, but we tried to be thankful that he was out, and that he had an opportunity to rest and get stronger.

I reported my concerns back to Quarriers, and one of the consultants gave us an extra appointment, and put Colin's keppra up. We continued on. The person Colin had been before he went into Quarriers seemed gone. He didn't read any more. He seemed very distant and detached. He was confused. His seizures became more. I phoned Quarriers with my concerns, but he already had had an extra appointment, and we were told to wait it out. On Andrew's second birthday, Colin seemed to be slowing down altogether. He was hardly speaking, his movements were slow, only his eyes showed any signs of responsiveness. I left the birthday party, and we all managed to get Colin very slowly along the drive into the car (about 10 feet), as we had an appointment at Quarriers – a follow up appointment to see how the keppra was working, as it was a relatively new drug. When we got there, the consultant took one look at Colin and realised that there was something badly wrong. Colin's keppra was put up again, and we were told if there was any deterioration to call her immediately. On the way home, I noticed Colin's fingers making strange repetitive movements. They worsened overnight. Colin did not get any better, and by the next morning, he was verbally unresponsive, and his feet were moving repetitively – forward and back. The consultant made sure there was a bed for Colin in a neuro ward, and we phoned an ambulance straightway. They put him on oxygen, and admitted him.

Colin was unresponsive to the spoken word – but all his limbs were randomly moving in some kind of circle or rapid movement. Watching him, the movement was strangely beautiful – like an amazing dance – yet also potentially deadly. Colin had no control over what was happening to him, no awareness whatsoever. He was given an EEG*[13] to see if it was epilepsy related! From what they said, I had the impression it was Complex Partial Status,*[14] and they gave him massive amounts of phenobarbitone*[15] to damp down the seizure activity.

Next time I visited, Colin was completely still – silent, unresponsive, drugged but comfortable, exhausted after all the movement, his whole system on stop for the first time for 2 days. He was in a room by himself, and I felt conscious of what I was wearing as I walked along the corridor, of the echoing sound of my footsteps. I felt a bit detached – it felt a bit as if I was watching someone else living out these experiences, and that it wasn't really me – as if I would wake up and find it was all a bad dream. Outside I thought I heard the consultant talking to a junior doctor – the phrase I heard was 'had psychotic episodes in the past'. I was angry; the consultant might be excellent at trying to find the right medication to help Colin, but I didn't understand why he thought now his epilepsy was connected to psychotic episodes.*[16] It was only years later, that I realised that seizure activity could cause psychosis – I so wish someone would have explained this to me earlier.

After a few days, Colin became more aware. One of the nurses showered and shaved him. He was discharged on his new medication – phenobarbitone and tegretol retard.*[17]

New beginnings with our new born son were wonderful, but shadows over Colin's health were gathering.

CHARCOAL DRAWING OF ANDREW, BY COLIN

Appendix 1

A THREE DIMENSIONAL WORLD

' Chess is the gymnasium of the mind.'

Blaise Pascal

As we have seen earlier, Colin often thought in a three dimensional manner. He dreamed in three dimensions, and was very creative. An example of this, was his concept of three dimensional chess. He created an eight level board out of wood and eight plastic squares, and he often played, and would teach anyone else who listened. It was an important part of his identity, and woe betide anyone who knocked his chess squares over!

I have included Colin's philosophy of thinking about this, but have left out the technicalities of how it was worked out in practice. Colin had all this worked out in great detail however, and often invited people to play.

THREE DIMENSIONAL CHESS CONCEPT – as written by Colin

From the middle ages and long before, warfare was fought on a basis of direct contact with one's opponent, whole nations could be won or lost in a single battle, yet more important were the politics around such events. A Lord with lands questioning loyalty to his King because of a family dispute, or perhaps a religious matter that has the country split in half. The original game of chess reflects this with the way strategies are used to gain control of the board, to take and lose pieces, the sacrifice of others for your advantage your opponent hasn't seen, the constant threat of check and checkmate which can turn a game around and win or lose it.

The world's entry into the new millennium has heralded many changes, especially where the even rapidly expanding and multiplying boundaries of science are concerned, often embracing concepts that a few years previously were regarded as science-fiction. A 'global economy'; politics ever more complicated with a single move having so many subsequent consequential effects; warfare, with two World Wars behind us, has the potential for ever greater mass destruction yet continues to be fought on many small battlefields around the world which the larger nations choose to take notice of according to their economic and political interests. But still the individual soldier is in a water filled mud-hole with dropping temperatures, wishing he could be home and will be survive tomorrow's attack? A pawn in a political game where he is required to play his part but will never understand the overall strategy of his superiors. That is the game of chess.

3D chess evolved from the original game, an attempt to represent the complexities of the modern world in a more complex game whilst preserving the basic rules of play and the original concept of the game.

In theory it would be possible to have an unlimited number of dimensions, but not in actual practice, which is why the original game with the 8 square board was used as boundaries of description and to ensure the preservation of the original image of chess.

In the midst of all his moods and states of wellness, Colin loved to challenge people to a game of chess, especially a three dimensional one! It soothed his brain, and reminded him that he was an original human being, and had value. His chess board became a proud symbol of his creativity and proud individualism! He had all the rules carefully worked out, and enjoyed exploring all the possible variety of moves.

Chapter 6

SHADOWS DEEPEN, SEIZURES WORSEN

'No pit is so deep, that God's love is not deeper.'

Corrie Ten Boom

'You cannot appreciate the strength of the anchor until you go through the storm.'

Anonymous

In the months after Colin coming out of hospital, he had patches of time where he seemed a bit better. I was hopeful that these would become the norm, and that the darker more impaired days would dwindle.

It had been recognised for a long time, that Colin was unfortunate, in that he did not have a seizure and then recover quickly. Rather he is 'post-ictal' *[18] for days afterwards. This means that he goes through a *pattern* rather like the following after a seizure:

The seizure starts with a guttural cry, that I am pre-programmed to be attentive to from anywhere round the house. Then there will be limb jerking, loss of bladder control, the face gradually changing colour (pale and then often a grey/ blue), an eventual settlement of movement, and deep and noisy gasps for breath, which gradually quieten. This whole process can take just about 30 seconds, but the consequences are profound. They often go like this:

Day one – Colin sleeps till mid-day, very passive and non-responsive, especially verbally. Does little for himself, except going to the toilet.

Day two – sleeps late, may try to speak a little, might switch the TV on to watch something. Might make a cup of tea.

Day three – more aware and responsive, but often irritable as he begins to realise that he hasn't been able to do everything he should.

Day four – irritable again because he is aware that he has had another seizure, and quite cross. He is more able to do things for himself, e.g. a game of chess, or to put a piece of quiche in the microwave. Can be quite depressed, as he realises he has been unwell.

Day five – his mood a bit more even, his brain functioning better, able to express his opinions, and showing more awareness of basic social conventions – e.g. might offer to make someone else a cup of tea.

After a while, it became clear that Colin was averaging six seizures a month. As there are on average 30 days in a month, this meant that he was usually somewhere in the above cycle of recovery from seizure almost every day. Sometimes Colin had two seizures together, maybe half an hour apart. This meant that each of the above stages was longer and more intense, but also might mean that he would have a respite at the end of the time, where he might have a couple of more highly functioning days. We came to really treasure these days. People would ask how Colin was, and I would just say he was recovering, or 'up and down'. The problem was that there were no adequate words. How can you make conversation, and put such a complex medical and emotional history in words? Surely things would soon begin to even out, and his health would be better.

Another big issue was Colin's driving licence. They said that whilst Colin was in Quarriers having his medication changed, he would need to give up driving for that time. The regulations are that if you have a seizure when you are awake, then you need inform the DVLC and to hand in your licence, and that you need to be seizure free for two years (i.e. seizure free when awake, seizures in sleep are treated differently) to get it back. Colin's seizures had all been when he was asleep before, but his period of seizure activity in the hospital seemed to mean that he couldn't drive now for two years. This was a big blow to Colin. He had been highly trained in his days of military intelligence – e.g. advanced driving course, and he loved driving. As for many men, it was a sign of his wellbeing and status in society. To not be able to drive was devastating. To be dependent on other people was also humiliating. He hated not being able to pop into the car to go down to the shops, or to see a friend. It was very depressing for him, a loss of identity – a very tangible sign of his inability to control anything in his life.

Colin loved cars, and took pride in his driving abilities, and this comes across in one of his favourite reminiscences – his pink jaguar story.

THE PINK JAGUAR STORY

The bright pink 4.2L engine firing on all five cylinders was making her way up the west coast of Scotland towards Glasgow. That the car was displaying Irish plates wasn't to be a problem until later when we ran into Strathclyde police.

I had been noticing for a while that the same cars were persistently following me all the way into Glasgow. It did panic me and I sped the rate of the car up, attempting to throw them off. I didn't manage to achieve this and ended up with helicopter surveillance and all roads with the potential for exit were blocked off by police cars, marked or unmarked.

The police officer who came to check me out asked for some means of personal identity. When I presented him with my warrant card of the SMIU he chuckled and said, 'Yeah, my kid gets these as well in his cereal packets.'

'That so (catching his eye)? I'd still advise you to check it out, either way you are going to get your arse kicked.' He walked away with a big smile on his face holding up the card in his hand. I sat back in my seat and relaxed, waiting for the police officer to return. This police officer who suspected that I was some kind of terrorist had never even bothered to check me for firearms – all the time I'd been carrying a 9mm Browning with a 12 capacity magazine in a leather shoulder holster. Had I been a genuine terrorist, I could have blown the police officer's head off at any time!

The police officer returned to my car practically crawling on all fours apologising for his ignorance concerning my warrant card. Somebody had evidently kicked the police officer's backside over the radio when he checked out my card and I had to say I relished every second of the police officer's discomfort.

We went away to the seaside for a few days holiday, and it was really tough. It was a long drive, and Colin had had a double seizure. He was very amicable, but not a lot of practical help. It was beginning to dawn on me that there were increasing number of days where I needed to do everything myself – pack the luggage, drive, look after Andrew, look after Colin, take responsibility for his medication, make the meals, get petrol for the car, make sure everything was ok. I was a complete failure trying to start a fire in the grate in the fireplace, and this meant we were a bit cold. There was no-one else to help, and the temptation was to feel very alone. Andrew in his 'Bob the builder' pyjamas and with his toy cars, was not the one to assist – even though he was confident that he could 'fix' anything. To give him his due, Andrew was willing to try! Knowing God was there in the midst of all of this also helped enormously, an anchor in the midst of the storm, as otherwise it could become overwhelming.

As Colin was having more seizures, I asked if his phenobarbitone could be put up, to see if this would help. The consultant was reluctant, but agreed. Colin was now on 90mg in the morning, and 90mg in the evening. This was worth a try, but bore no fruit. Colin's seizure rate continued at the same level, and all that happened is that there were days when he was so zombified, he barely even seemed to know where he was. I remember putting some dinner on the table, and Colin taking about 20 minutes to realise he was meant to eat it. The food was cold by this time. Yet you couldn't help him to eat it, as he would resent that kind of 'interference'. He would see it as someone taking away his independence or trying to control him and become agitated. He would rather do things slowly at his own pace, to make his own choices, and to take his time.

Although the combination of seizures and medication slowed Colin down dramatically, I'm not sure how far he realised this – he just thought everyone else was going very fast and he was impatient. He had a few double seizures – say 1am and 3am, and sometimes sleeping well into the evening afterwards – till 7pm, up for food and drink, and then back to sleep. Just not a life.

At the next appointment with the consultant, Colin's medication was put down again, and he talked about the possibility of a vagus nerve stimulator[*19] being implanted into Colin. This was a kind of pace-maker for the brain, trying to regulate the electrical input in Colin's brain through his vagus nerve. The stimulator might help reduce seizures, and also the length and intensity of the post-ictal phase. This seemed like a good possibility. At the time, Colin had been watching the film 'Bicentennial Man' about the place of artificial intelligence and robotics in people. He felt a bit unsure about having a metallic implant, but he knew it might help. There was a sense of a gradual erosion of identity, and of things being out with his control. Yet Colin was willing to try – his bravery never failed.

Meanwhile Colin was put on trileptal as a tertiary anti-convulsant,[*20] to see if this would help. The dose was gradually built up over time, but there was no obvious impact. Colin had a few infections and colds and things, which usually resulted in him being sluggish and slow. There was also concern about his feet. It had been hoped that when he came off phenytoin, that Colin's feet would improve and the neuropathy or lack of feeling would lift. However that did not seem to have happened, and this had started to make his walking a bit more difficult. He also seemed to be a bit off in his balance sometimes.

Everyone was helping, my mum and Colin's mum and dad, and they were patient and caring, but it was quite a strain. I wondered if we could get extra support from somewhere. It was hard to get Colin to have a shower, as he just wasn't focussed enough. Sometimes he forgot to take his medication, and I had to monitor it all the time – he took his tablets at 10ish in the morning, and the same at night. Taking his tablets a few hours too late could precipitate a seizure. Episodically, Colin was also acting out of character – like the day he was hungry, and ate three packets of crisps and two chocolate bars. (Colin didn't even like chocolate). Colin seemed to be becoming increasingly confused between seizures, and the trilpetal was gradually taken down and away. His phenobarbitone was also lowered a little, and although there were some withdrawal seizures, and mood swings etc, Colin remained stable at six seizures a month.

We tried to do things to help Colin pursue his interests. He bought a new computer, so he could write out his memories. We got a befriender from a local epilepsy charity, Epilepsy Connections, and that worked out really well. The charity helped us think about many things – about a local art class, about the possibility of homeopathic remedies, of applying for Disability Living Allowance. All very practical, and needing to be done.

It was strange talking to Colin, and with him not always being able to respond. Sometimes it was almost like he was not there altogether. Physically we were all in the room, but emotionally and intellectually, Colin was not there. It could make me feel very alone. I could be unwell, and Colin wouldn't really notice, never mind try to help. If I was being sick, Colin would just walk over me – it was like he wasn't there, just completely absorbed in his own wee world. Sometimes I felt as if I wasn't there either.

I told Andrew, 'There are days that daddy doesn't feel very well, but he still loves you very much.' As a wee boy, Andrew was very aware that his dad slept a lot, and on other days was very loud and shouty. There were other days, when the 'old' Colin was still about – still supporting the SNP, still reading the *Economist* and enjoying a good film. There were days when he had a good conversation about how the family is doing, and when he played well with Andrew – building towers with lego etc. Yet I started to be more aware, and to think, when is all this going to change for the better? Colin was on the waiting list for the stimulator, hopefully that would make the difference.

We went on holiday. Another coastal town. We went down on the beach in the rain, and there was a missing dog, and we tried to help find him. Colin slipped on the rocks and twisted his ankle. A visit to the local hospital revealed it was badly strained, and he ended up on elbow crutches. When we got back home, Colin's parents had hoovered the carpets, and cut the grass and left fresh flowers in a vase. It was a lovely surprise, and much appreciated.

Andrew's third birthday in August 2003 went well, and helped to redeem the previous year's birthday! Colin had a good day, and Andrew was able to open his presents with both parents there – in contrast to the previous year. It was great, just such a relief.

September 2003 – Colin had four seizures in two days. It looked like something was way off. I called out the local GP, and Colin was put on oxygen in the ambulance and taken to hospital. They discharged him, saying he was ok. Later on that night, Colin was still far from well – confused, disorientated unresponsive, and I phoned the out of hours service. They said there were no beds at the Victoria, but there were some at the Southern, and so Colin was admitted there. He was having temperature spikes and random repetitive movements of the hands etc – Colin was put on diazepam*[21] and admitted him to the ward. Colin was still showing seizure activity, and more intravenous ant-convulsants were given. Eventually everything dampened down, and he was quiet. He was moved to another ward. The next day I went to see him. I phoned the nurses first of all, and said that I would like to bring our three year old son. Was Colin well enough to see him? They said that there was no problem, that 'Colin had had a shower and was comfortable'.

When I got there, Colin opened his eyes and started to speak. He said things like 'I believe in God', 'I am a robot', 'they have cut off my legs and replaced them with motorised legs', 'why is no-one answering my questions?' I felt deeply frustrated and angry – was this really an ideal enviroment to bring a young child? Why did the nurses not tell me that Colin was disorientated– don't say they hadn't noticed? When I spoke to them, they shrugged and were dismissive – they had not noticed any problems. It felt as if it was me that had the problem – that was the implication. Why was Colin like this, what was going on? Fortunately Andrew was too young to pay much attention, and he played with his toys instead. Eventually after a couple of days the confusion passed, Colin became more alert and orientated and he was discharged. The questions remained. The consultant on the ward said he thought it was some kind of infection that caused it all, although the tests were inconclusive. This told me a lot!

Daily life continued. Someone started coming to do personal care twice a week – at just over £20 a go! Occupational Therapy (OT) provided a bath lift, and some handles for the bathroom. Life got tricky if I was not well, as looking after Andrew and caring for Colin was a little challenging. We had good family support from my mum and Colin's parents. Colin started having more double seizures. Each seizure is so awful, the sudden yell as it starts, the horrific jerking over his whole body, his eyes rolling, and his face turning that terrible grey colour. The violence of his seizures strangely seems to embody the violence and noise of his military traumas, raging out of his soul through his body. It often just last seconds, but the impact is so out of proportion to these moments.

Each seizure can be slightly different in form, longer, shorter, more noisy, less so – then there is the recovery period, when his breathing is very loud and laboured, and then becomes quieter. Sometimes he is incontinent and the bed needs changed. Sometimes he falls out of bed, and there are carpet burns all over one side of his face. I have medication (buccal midazolam)*[22] I can give if Colin seems in danger of having a second seizure – this is difficult to judge – maybe if he has a cold or stomach upset, or has taken his medication a bit late.

I decided that I needed to be a bit more pro-active. Rather than just encouraging people to pray for Colin, maybe I needed to take him for prayer. We believed that God heard our prayers, and that this was an area worth pursuing. I took Colin to a local preacher with gifts in the area of healing. Colin said he felt relaxed and peaceful after it, which was good.

In April 2003, we got a call to say that Colin could go forward to have his vagus nerve stimulator put in. It was a procedure that would just keep Colin in hospital overnight. The surgeon implanted the battery unit in Colin's chest, and the stimulator itself in his neck area. We were hopeful.

I waited anxiously at home, and the surgeon said that the procedure had gone without incident. On the day after the operation, the stimulator was switched on. Colin said it felt as if he has been choked every five minutes, as it constricted his throat. He was frustrated by the relentless nature of it. He seemed to be having problems adjusting at the beginning, as it comes on and off all the time. It was still at a very low setting. The next day he seemed a little brighter. I began to realise that Colin's short-term memory was really messed up. He couldn't remember where we went on holiday the previous year, he forgot the number on his Visa card, he told the befriender that he broke his ankle in Guatemala (it was really Glasgow). We kept going back to the hospital over a period of months to get the stimulator adjusted, i.e. turned up, when it should begin to work better.

After about six months, the results of having the stimulator were mixed. Colin got used to it, although he had occasional periods when it felt overwhelming. Sometimes it constricted his throat when he was trying to eat, and it caused him to choke. It also stopped him singing, as his voice kept going hoarse, and this prevented him singing in the choir any more. Colin's seizure rate remained at six a month, and his post-ictal periods did not seem to have changed much in character.

We started to think more about what we could do to make things better, and started doing detective work to see if we can find any pattern in Colin's seizures. After a number of Sundays in a row when Colin had seizures, we realised that caffeine was a culprit. Caffeine in coffee could definitely cause seizures, so Colin had to have decaf, especially in the evening. (Although needless to say, Colin really prefers caffeine – and completely subverted any advice, took it at every opportunity.) Another thing we noticed was that Colin often had seizures after Chinese food, so we had to give these up. After some internet searching, we realised that it was the MSG*[23] in the Chinese food that caused the problem, so we stopped having any form of food with MSG as far as possible. Curries also seemed to be a trigger sometimes, depending on where they were from, so we had them only very occasionally. We spoke to the consultant about these things, and he said that we didn't really have to give these up, for they only really changed the pattern of the seizures, rather than cause additional seizures, but there was something very deep inside which makes you want to avoid anything which gives seizures, so we stopped. We had to learn to live in a whole new way, and it was very painful – to give up things that we enjoyed.

Chapter 7

TOGETHER ON A ROLLER-COASTER

'The *I* in illness is isolation, and the crucial letters in wellness are *we*.'

Author unknown, quoted in Mimi Guarneri, *The Heart Speaks: A Cardiologist Reveals the Secret Language of Healing*

'My life, my career has been like a roller-coaster. I've either been an enormous success or just a down-and-out failure.'

Judy Garland

'Most of the important things in the world have been accomplished by people who have kept on trying when there seemed to be no hope at all.'

Dale Carnegie

After a period of chronic illness, Colin no longer got appointments with the consultant at the hospital. Colin was told that he only needed appointments with the nurses – to get his vagal nerve stimulator checked. At the time, we thought that made sense. However there was another covert message from the medical profession underneath – we can do nothing more. They didn't want to change Colin's anti-convulsants, saying that if they tried to, and it made things worse, then putting the medication back to the previous level might not be effective any longer.

Colin was on his medication, his vagal nerve stimulator was working, but he was still having six seizures a month. They could be clustered different ways. Sometimes he didn't have any for 14 days, and by day 7/8 his standard of life was getting better and better. It was great to get some of his character back, his desire to see a film, or to help in the garden. And yet as he grew brighter, the threat of the next seizure loomed ahead. We were very careful not to expect or anticipate this – we didn't want to provide some kind of subliminal trigger. Yet one night, there would come the seizure, and usually another one reasonably soon afterwards, and so we fell into another downward spiral.

I know it was only Colin who had the seizures, but it affected my life and the life of the family in such a decisive way, it felt as if we were all going up and down all the time. It was indeed a roller-coaster ride, one minute being on a high with Colin in reasonable form, and then crashing the next minute into a place of dark unresponsiveness and eggshell like irritability.

It was impossible to plan, for we could never tell how Colin would be on any day. We could only ever plan something, knowing you might have to cancel it. I remember going to a children's concert with Andrew; Colin wasn't great, but he seemed reasonable so we all set out. We managed to park, and make our way through the crowded lobby to our allocated seats. Unfortunately, behind us sat a mum and her kids, and the kids were very restless. They were jumping up and down, and tapping the seats in front where we sat, making them vibrate, and you could see that Colin was becoming stressed by the noise and the intrusion in his space. Eventually he turned round, and shouted 'shut up' in his most fierce voice and menacing voice. The children went quiet. The mum was outraged, shouting, 'How dare you say this to my children, I'm putting in a complaint, people like you shouldn't be allowed out.' She went and spoke to a steward, who transferred her family to another row. Not a very stress free afternoon. What was the answer – should we just stay in all day?

This leads to a whole topic of how to help someone with a neurological impairment to have the best quality of life, as society is not very tolerant of people who think differently, or act in bizarre ways. As a result of his military experiences, Colin always reacts badly to loud noise – as his instincts tell him that it is a bomb going off, or a bullet flying his way, and he hits the deck or goes for his gun. His startle reflex is very strong, and he can get very upset if there are crowds or noise or bustle. However as time went on, Colin seemed even more upset by these events. For some of the time, Colin was quite amiable in his unwellness, on days when he was not able to think or reason clearly as to what is going on. However there could be times when he became very grumpy and would swear and shout, and it seemed better for him not to leave the house at all. Often we could not work out which way he would go, so risk management became impossible.

Socialisation is another related issue, as Colin could get very cross or his mood could change suddenly for no particularly external reason. People are not very tolerant of this kind of mood change. This means that you are doing intuitive risk assessments all the time, trying to work out if on a given day, Colin is likely to benefit from meeting others, and if the other people present are broad minded enough to cope with whatever might happen. In the midst of this process, you can lose a lot of friends, and gain a few others who are supportive and understanding. I have erred on the cautious side in this area, as the upset that can be caused from things going wrong is so great!

Sometimes I have wondered if I should have taken risks with more people, but you can only wonder this with hindsight. For all people who know a friend or relative caring for someone who is not well: if you can, please take a while to listen to them and offer some support. And if the unwell person becomes agitated or has an outburst, don't act as if this is a personal insult to you. It really isn't – the person is just interpreting their environment through a damaged emotional and cognitive lens, and so anything can happen. It seems natural to them, even if not to anyone else. This kind of situation can be very isolating for those involved, and sensitive and/or prayerful support can mean such a lot. The people who have journeyed with us over the years have been such a wonderful support and encouragement, and helped keep us sane.

COLIN AT CHRISTMAS

The home visiting team came to do personal care with Colin twice a week. We got to meet a lot of memorable and lovely people, who were very helpful. However sometimes the staff were not well trained for the situations that they found themselves in. It took staff a long time to suss Colin out – his strong likes and dislikes, his moods and ups and downs, but usually once they did, things were fine. However from time to time the management of the care service would decide to move everyone around. This could have disastrous consequences, as the people who knew Colin well would disappear, and a new lot would show up. Girls working for the carer's organisation would come along and would come to the door, and say to me things like 'Hello, I'm here to see your father'. As he had been dead for many years, this seemed a neat trick and I always wondered how they would manage this. Then I would have to explain that no, it wasn't my father, but my husband they were here to care for. Often the significance of this distinction didn't seem to really penetrate.

Another new woman carer decided that Colin was taking too long having his shower and she pressed him to be quicker. Colin felt completely 'got at' and told her in no uncertain terms what she could do. She was completely taken aback and affronted at being treated like this. There was a major incident, as it was reported, and everyone came in to assess the situation, but fortunately the person in charge knew Colin and the woman, and understood that she had treated him in an inappropriate way, and she didn't come back. We found that patient, laid back male workers got on best with Colin, and over the years those who built up good relationships with him had a lot of fun.

Around 2004-6, the very helpful local occupational therapist referred Colin to the local hospital Physical Disability Team (PDT), for some support. The people in the team were very professional and thoughtful, a psychologist, an OT, a physiotherapist etc. They worked with Colin to help him do as much for himself as possible – e.g. to help him remember how to make meals. He used to be a great cook, and they helped him make an omelette and chilli and things. However Colin didn't try by himself afterwards. He did once try to do beans on toast whilst I was out, and put the beans under the grill in their tin – after this, I felt maybe it would be better not to encourage Colin to cook by himself! The potential for catastrophe was enormous.

The psychologist worked with Colin, doing cognitive behavioural work, which was good. The only thing was that Colin didn't always remember from session to session what had been going on at the last appointment, so he wasn't always able to benefit from these sessions as much as you might want. A physiotherapist came out to work with Colin. She pointed out that he had difficulty with proprioception – i.e. his perception of depth. This was helpful, as it helped me understand why if Colin went to make a cup of tea, he usually filled the kettle and the cup right up to the brim, or even over it. It also explained why he had difficulty with steps, sometimes missing his footing. The part of his brain that deals with measuring depth seemed to have stopped functioning.

Another issue that was influential was that the lack of feeling in Colin's feet and legs did not recede, as had been hoped. Instead, it meant that Colin felt he walked 'with penguin feet', with less and less feeling in them the more he walked. He lifted his feet quite high when walking, and had a loss of balance which meant he often fell over. Even just in the bedroom, trying to get to the bathroom, sometimes, he would knock into the furniture, and everything would end up on the floor, which didn't help his mood.

The purpose of the PDT team turned out to be only for short term interventionist rehabilitative work. They did what they could, but eventually they had to close Colin's file. They passed us back to the Social Work department, and a lovely social worker came out to see us a few times in 2007. She was very helpful, and helped us work through issues like how to get a disabled badge for the car, to apply for higher rate DLA, and to get power of attorney for Colin. It was hard work, and a lot of form filling, but she was indefatigable, and worked hard with us. Then she said we were being transferred to someone else, and we didn't hear from anyone for a long time. She was a lovely example of someone in the system who did make a difference – one individual who was both compassionate and whose helpful intervention brought much fruit.

As we began to realise that the medics were finished, we had a desire to try to find healing for Colin in complementary medicines. A local epilepsy charity suggested we go to the local homeopathic hospital. There was a long waiting list. When we went there, we always saw a very nice man, who assured us that homeopathy could help. Colin tried all kinds of potions, with names like *nux moche*, and krypton, but there was no discernible difference. Colin didn't always like taking the powder, which didn't help matters either. Some months he would seem a little better, but then the next month would be a little worse, and so it went on. There were so many 'false dawns' that it just became part of the pattern. He did like taking krypton, as the analogies with Superman were very positive, even though the negative part was that it was krypton that took Superman's energy away!

We went to see Jan de Vries (a well respected naturopath) in his clinic, and he gave us many bottles of things for us to take, and told us that Colin should avoid cheese. Colin stopped eating cheese (which he loved) for about four years, but as that seemed to have no effect whatsoever, he started again. Again there was no difference in Colin's condition, and we stopped going.

We also went to see a nutritionist for a while. Colin had tried taking a general multivitamin tablet, but it seemed to provoke seizures, so we stopped. In general, we were trying to eat more healthily – more vegetables and fruit. The nutritionist did a hair sample, and looked up the internet, and suggested various supplements. Magnesium deficiency was a possible cause of seizures, so Colin started to take magnesium tablets. The amino acid taurine[*24] was another supplement recommended, and again Colin took this for a couple of years. At the beginning, Colin seemed slightly better, but then relapsed into his usual patterns. We did improve our nutrition overall which was good, and we did try to see if these supplements would help. Even if it was just to eliminate this as a helpful idea worth exploring, it was worth doing. There is little scientific evidence to show that complementary healing strategies work, but there is often little funding for such research in the first place, so it is hard to evaluate. When someone is very sick you want to explore all reasonable options – just in case!

As Christians, we wondered if there was a spiritual root for Colin's seizures, and so we pursued various types of prayer. We went to the Acorn Healing Trust, and people prayed for us. We also visited the Bield, where Marianne and Robin Anker-Petersen always welcomed us, and prayed and showed us great hospitality – a place of quietness and peace. Colin always experienced a 'quickening' during prayer, in that his spirit would seem to respond, he became more alert, more animated, more relaxed. This was always lovely to see. I had heard Francis and Judith McNutt speak at a conference in Perth and then in Edinburgh. We went over to Jacksonville in Florida to Christian Healing Ministries, run by Francis and Judith McNutt.

This was a big step of faith, as I had never been to Florida, never driven in America, didn't know anyone there, and had no idea what to expect. Andrew and I have vivid memories of me trying to drive from the airport at Sanford to the hotel in Orlando, with me not realising that if you stay in the left hand lane on the Interstate, your keep coming off at all the exits, as there was no choice to keep straight on the road. It meant an hour's journey took four hours, and we went past the Orange County Convention Centre more times than I care to remember, as I sought to get to our wee hotel. I remember gritting my teeth every new time we went past, the only consolation being that we were in roughly the same wrong place. Going anywhere with a four year old child and a grumpy husband was often a great challenge, as in reality I was often having to make decisions and adapt, without much input from anyone else. Relying on prayer was key for every moment, just to survive.

Yet it was a great experience going to Christian Healing Ministries, where a team of people prayed with Colin for healing. They tried to discern if there was a reason as to why this had happened to Colin – the result of a trauma from the past, historical family patterns, lack of forgiveness or false beliefs about himself, ongoing inner battles. They were gentle and sensitive, and their love and ability to listen was restorative in itself, and over the days, you could see Colin's spirit grow in strength and brighten. We had some wonderful holidays over in Florida, going to CHM for part of the time. It became an annual event, and always very positive. And we got to know some wonderful people there, some of whom are still our friends – amazingly enough. Johanna and David Baker became family, and we are grateful to them every day for their gracious friendship and love. They always loved us, and were so thoughtful and gracious in their generosity and compassion to these people over from Scotland, even 16 years later. They never failed to be understanding, patient, accepting, thoughtful, and kind. Such a wonderful blessing. Over the years we have been so privileged to meet wonderful people who walked with us, on a difficult and dark path, and their prayerful friendship and love were so meaningful and encouraging. A wee saying is that 'Someone will keep going tomorrow because you prayed for them tonight' and the power of prayer has often been felt – preventing disaster, calming someone at the right moment, encouraging you when everything seemed to fall apart.

However, though Colin might be seizure free for a bit longer, or brighter in his spirit, or a bit more integrated in his identity for a while, the seizures would come back, and all became lost again. The second time we went, Colin had a good 14 days without a seizure, and this was especially wonderful, as we got to do lots of things as a family – to go round the theme parks, to swim, to explore different parts of Florida. A wonderful blessing, and great memories.

People in Glasgow prayed for us also. A couple came, and said that they felt that God wanted them to come and pray for Colin every week. They had three people who they felt led to pray for. This wonderful couple came and prayed most Monday evenings for Colin for a year. It was a considerable part of their time, and we were very grateful. They prayed everything they could think of, inner vows, family tree healing, demon possession, standing on God's promises, and again often Colin would be responsive. He was grateful for having people that would listen to all his military experiences, people who were loving and patient. Yet by the end of the year, although Colin was pleased to have the attention, his seizure rate was much the same. The two other people that the couple prayed for both died – peaceful deaths, reconciled to God, but they died. And the couple decided to stop coming, and we were left alone again.

Now and again over the years we have gone to different Christian healing meetings. Mostly they have been very helpful, praying, loving people who have been kind and encouraging. Now and again people say more difficult things however, like: 'If your faith was stronger, this wouldn't have happened'; 'there must be some spiritual root of sin that has caused this that you have not looked at'; 'you need to really believe God's promises and stand upon them or nothing will happen'. These are not words remotely helpful to anyone.

Of course it is good to be open to look at any potential cause of illness, and we need to be realistic in doing this. Yes, we need to be positive about the future, and to believe that God can heal. But to tell someone who has been chronically sick for many years these kind of clichés is hurtful and simply alienates the people who are suffering. Most of our experiences of Christian healing have not been like this, but every now and again someone pops up and says something well motivated but hurtful and overly simplistic.

I guess too, in retrospect, I wonder if Colin could have been better supported as a veteran? This is a difficult question, for often Colin was proud and didn't find it easy to acknowledge any form of need. Yet could there not have been some way of offering him counselling or medical support at some point, which would have helped him to know that his years of service were recognised, and to at the very least acknowledge his struggles? Every now and again, we made touch with a potentially supportive organisation, but despite a lot of goodwill, very little of practical use seemed to come from it.

Chapter 8

NAVIGATING THE JOURNEY

– AND AIRPORTS!

We seemed to be on a long journey – the title of a book I read recently called it 'suffering in slow motion',[1] and I like that as a description. It seemed very apt, because everything, good and bad, seems to happen painstakingly slowly – over many months.

When I think of our experiences of travelling, and going away, I need to talk a little about some of the particular experiences we had in this realm. We used to go to hotels now and again, and this could work reasonably well. However there were problems. For example, they usually stop serving breakfast at 10am. For Colin, on medication which resulted in him being sleepy, and sometimes needing to sleep extra after a seizure, this was not good. So many times, we would rush down to breakfast at 9.55am trying to get there on time. Colin loves his food, so this was worthwhile, but we were all pretty grouchy by the time we got down there, unwashed, half dressed and in fact barely conscious.

On other days it was too difficult, and we just missed breakfast. Mealtimes generally were difficult, as another thing that has become harder with time, was choosing the food. Colin would be given a menu with six choices for a starter, 12 choices for a main course, four choices for a sweet. On some days it is too hard to ask him to do this. I have seen him sit for 20 minutes looking at a menu, slowly thinking, and then unable to choose. And another person cannot help him, for that is seen as interference, taking control away, and so he would react against this fiercely. Sometimes we have had to leave, and just get fish and chips from the shop down the road.

---

1 Pamela C. Kennedy and Richard Kennedy, *Suffering in Slow Motion: help for a long journey through dementia and other terminal illnesses.*

We used to go to a lovely flat in Millport, and Colin loved playing crazy golf, or having some food and looking at the sea. On one famous occasion, I had to drive Colin's parents back on the ferry to Largs, and Andrew age four was in the back seat. We took them back to their car, in the car park in Largs, but when we turned round, the last ferry had just left. There was no way back across to Millport; Andrew and I eventually found the last available room in a wee hotel in Largs. The flat in Millport didn't have a phone, so I could not contact Colin to let him know what had happened. I considered phoning the police on the island, to go up to the flat to let Colin know that we were all right, but it would be traumatic for him to have the police at the door. So we stayed in Largs overnight, and then got one of the first ferries back the next morning. I rushed up the stairs and got into the flat – worried about Colin. Of course, he was sound asleep, and hadn't even noticed we were not there the night before!

Flying has been another difficult experience. We have gone to Florida most years, because we have wonderful friends there, space, prayer, access to expertise in a number of healing and positive areas. This however needs a ten hour flight. This in itself can be stressful, especially if the airline is not on the ball. On one flight, it was taking ages to check in, and when we eventually got to the front desk, they no longer had three seats together, so we had to agree to be split up, although one of the seats was only a few rows behind the others. We did remind them that one of our party had a disability. That made no difference. This created a certain anxiety within me, for Colin was a bit woozy – just a few days after a seizure.

When we got on the plane, it quickly became apparent that quite a few families were split up, and that this was a major issue for more families than just us. The crew tried to sort it all out, but in the end the captain made an announcement saying there was a mum and her two children and they were all seated in different places, and that until somebody volunteered to swap with them, then the plane was not leaving. There was lots of moans and groans, and then the two people sitting in Colin's row, decided that they would give up their seats, as would the man sitting beside them because he wasn't with anyone! Colin ended up about 12 rows in front, far away from the two of us. I spoke to the head of the flight crew, and explained the difficulty, and that Colin wasn't very well, that he could have a seizure. The head steward said not to worry, it would all be fine, and that as a recognition of all that we had been through, we would all get free complementary orange juice for the whole flight! As an example of how people treat those with disabilities, it was priceless. In one way it is funny, but in another way it is tragic – and so stressful as to what the consequence could have been.

Another aspect of flying, was that we needed to confirm with our insurance company that Colin could fly, and have a letter for the airline saying that he was fit to fly. The first letter that the GP gave us said that Colin was fit to fly, as long as he had not had a seizure in the previous 24 hours. This was absolutely devastating in its consequences, for it meant that we never knew if we were going anywhere till we got on the plane. The worst thing about our first trip to Florida was being up all night the night before, praying that Colin wouldn't have a seizure, so we could leave. And the same coming back. The strange thing was too, that actually if Colin had just had a seizure, then it meant that he was much less likely to have one on the plane, and surely that was a bonus.

The next time we were thinking of going on holiday, the GP was off, and we had an appointment to see the consultant a few weeks before we flew, so we asked him to do a fit to fly letter, and he did one in more general terms. This was great. Colin did actually have a seizure the night before we flew, but it made no difference to him flying, except that he was slower going through security. The next year, we had to go through the process again. The GP told us that he was following BMC (British Medical Council) guidelines, but in the end kindly phrased it on the letter 'that we were advised not to fly within 24 hours of a seizure' and this gave us a certain latitude. I spoke to a number of Epilepsy charities to find out the reason for such a prohibition on flying within 24 hours after a seizure, but no one could tell me anything.

Stories about airports abound. There was the time Colin was very slow and unresponsive, and we had to go through security in Sandford. He had to take his shoes off, and he could never go through the security gate because of his vagal nerve stimulator which might have malfunctioned in the same way as a pacemaker (we had another letter for that), and instead he had a body search. It took us ages to get through security, but everyone was very nice, and it all happened. Just then there was an announcement over the tannoy, to ask us to go back to the bookings desk to sort out an anomaly (someone had not crosschecked one of the details from our passports). We all had to go back – it took 30 seconds to sort out at the desk, and then we spent 30 minutes all going through security again. It was so difficult to go through all this again, and the staff kindly let us get on with it, without putting any pressure on us. We were really so thankful to eventually get on the plane with no incidents.

At airports, there is not really good provision for people with hidden disabilities. Colin would not have easily accepted help, but airports at this time were also less likely to provide anything other than a wheelchair. The stress levels, especially around the security gates are high, and so another year, again on the Florida side, Colin lost his wallet. He thought he had put it down in the security area, and we had to report this to the police. A lovely young policeman – about 6 foot 6 and looking about 16 came to help. The policeman helpfully said that he lost his wallet all the time, and that's why he now didn't carry one anymore. I had to phone to cancel Colin's cards, which was another great position to be in, as I was not the named cardholder. One of the attendants said he would help me look for the missing wallet, and I had to leave Colin and Andrew in the international departure lounge, whilst the attendant took me back to security to see if anything had been handed in.

This process took for ages, and then I realised that I was now on the wrong side of the security gates, and that I didn't have my passport with me, as I had left it back with Colin and Andrew. The attendant went rushing back to them to get it, whilst I stood there, conscious that our flight was due to get called to its gate soon. The attendant did come back, and I got through security. Whilst we were chatting, it turned out that it was his second week working there. We were back just in time for the flight to be called. The stress of going though airports was phenomenal, as we never knew how Colin would be.

Meanwhile, we lived each day, wondering how things would develop. By the autumn of 2006, Colin had not been in hospital for a couple of years; no infections, no multiple seizures; it looked like I should have been celebrating that things looked a bit better – yet I felt uneasy. Had things always been like this? Colin managed about 3 out of 10 writing classes on a Thursday, as he was just too ill to go. He had developed the habit of often eating standing up, as if he had forgotten he had the ability to sit down. Sometimes, after a 'bad' seizure, it could take 20-30 minutes for him to respond to an invitation – would you like to come through to dinner? We all learned just to start eating, and Colin would appear when it registered in his brain, and he decided to come through.

In December, we had an appointment with the epilepsy nurses – I thought that maybe I could take the opportunity to ask some questions. Colin was there too, and spoke a little, and they said it was good to hear him speak. I say that Colin's seizure rate is steady – six a month, but I feel he is not so well – that I'm not sure if he is just the same, or if my perception that he might not be so good as he was, might be correct. They don't want to comment, but eventually one says the latter is likely to be more accurate of the two. Colin does not catch it, the exchange is so quick – thank goodness. But these words, which I asked to hear, seem to have changed everything. It is all so clear – he is deteriorating. It is not my imagination, or my own projected fears. It is the reality, and the reality all along. How could I have missed this? Because I believed that healing was always the option round the next corner, and that we just needed to prayerfully wait. I kept positive and hopeful and this was a wonderful focus, but it masked what was really happening.

In the spring of 2007 – life was busy. We ended up having to do some repairs on our wee house, and it was very arduous and time consuming. A counsellor worked with me, very kindly – she said she had experience of similar situations, and that Colin's condition was getting worse, for that is what happens if you have this number of grand mal seizures a month. He was not just treading water, and I became aware that each seizure was potentially causing greater damage. I talked to people round about – Colin's parents, but they were not sure. It felt as if only I was facing the truth. I recognised too that I had become more detached – Colin had become a person to support and help and to care for, but his identity as a husband seemed to be strangely obscure. I felt kind of numb.

Little things, almost imperceptibly, were changing. Colin hardly ever went up to his study any more. He used to go up, and it was his own wee room for watching dvds, and having his own space. Now he was seldom there, he stayed downstairs instead. When he spoke to people, at times it was like there was no volume control, for he spoke loudly and harshly, and then he would laugh, as if to say, 'I don't know if I meant it as it sounds'. I would bring him a cup of tea, and he would turn round and growl menacingly, 'Why would I want this?' as if I had delivered the worst insult in the world. Yet he hated answering questions or making decisions – it was too hard. He didn't have all the information available to make the right answers anyway, and that just frustrated him, and he snapped back. Well meaning people would ask questions like, 'When did you serve in the army?' and Colin would blink at them and stare, either not answering, or guessing boldly but wildly incorrectly, or occasionally getting it exactly right.

Yet what could help? I kept praying – as Colin was less alert and seemed quite remote. Perhaps the answer lay in physical stuff, some kind of body work? Instead of involving speech and verbal skills, maybe a way of communicating directly to Colin's body would be a better route. I hear of sacral cranial work,*25 and there is a practitioner in Glasgow. I phone up, and we go to meet Marion. She is kind and listens – to our words, but also to Colin's body. Colin is having a bad day – it is hard. Yet she works with him , and he seems more relaxed. Then he has a seizure afterwards. And the same the next week, and the next. Part of me despairs. Another part rejoices – for some kind of connection must be being made for this to happen. About the fourth session, the seizures stopped the day of the sessions, and Colin seemed to benefit for a while. Marion did some water work with Colin in the pool, and this was also very relaxing for him, to help his body release some of the stress and tension of living.

Another opportunity presented itself, for there was a place where they offered intensive sacral cranial therapy – guess where? – Florida! We discovered that this kind of experience was offered by the Upledger Institute in Palm Beach Florida.*26 It was about 200 miles from where we have been before. An intensive week cost £2000 – for five days 10am to 5pm for treatment. It seemed like a remote hope, and yet I phoned to see what dates might be available – I phoned Darius a number of times, and he phoned back a number of times, and we kept missing each other. When it is hard to get hold of someone it is hard to tell if this is a sign not to go ahead, or opposition to something really helpful.

Eventually we get to talk, and there seems to be some possible dates in July. I then play E-mail tag with the office manager Sarah – who so kindly perseveres, even when our credit card does not work in the States, and everything has to be done three times. We get a place for Colin in July. Three weeks before the course, we are booking last minute flights and getting letters saying Colin is fit to fly, etc. Are we doing the right thing? What a lot of money! Will we get there this time?

ANDREW'S FIRST CAR

Love Song for a Wounded Warrior

Colin on his Birthday and in Florida

A Painting of 'Conflict' by Colin

All these thoughts were going round in my mind as we left Scotland. On the way out, Colin is grumpy and out of sorts – it is very stressful – I am hoping he will not be snappy with the wrong person e.g. the security guard at the airport. A few days before we fly, there is an attempted bombing of Glasgow airport. It makes our logistics more tricky – more walking from the taxi to the airport, to check in etc, but it is too late to ask for special assistance. When we arrive, the room is not ready in our hotel room – Colin is hot and bad tempered in the car. The hotel upgrades our room and apologises for the delay.

We go to Seaworld on the first day. It is so hot – Colin looks miserable. We wait in a 40 minute queue to see the dolphins. The fan Andrew thoughtfully bought, does not work. We are melting – whose bright idea was this? And yet we get to feed the dolphins – and Colin's eyes light up, and he looks as if an inner light has been switched on. He is happy to stroke them, and feed them fish. The staff takes photos, of this happy family together, playing with dolphins. And just for a while it is true – a comment of deep connection and beauty – another miracle.

We drive down to the Upledger Institute. Driving on the other side of the road in a part of Florida we have never been to before is scary. By another miracle we find the hotel without difficulty – it is right on the coast, and the situation is stunning. We go for a walk on the beach at dusk. There is a gorgeous sunset and we find ourselves in the middle of the release of baby turtles into the sea. We get to hold them, and to let them go, and watch as they head across the sand towards the waves. It is so beautiful, and typical of the unexpected joy and wonder that there is in the journey.

We went along on the first day to the Upledger Insitute, not knowing what to expect. We arrived just in time, due to the drawbridges we had to wait for, to let the boats pass on the route from the hotel to the Institute. We met four other people also enrolled in the programme – another family are also from Europe. Andrew and I expected to have to leave, but we were all included in the welcome and relaxation exercises. The people offering the therapy were really friendly. Over the week, they spoke to each of us in turn – offering support and space – and they even provided a dryer for our washing!

People were so kind. We were all interviewed separately – Andrew was very impressed because he got a free packet of Pokemon cards! The volunteers did a wide variety of therapies, some are Christians and offer prayer also – very quiet, very gentle. John Upledger came and spoke to Colin. And over the week, every day Colin seemed a bit brighter, a little less erascible. Such an amazing gift. One evening, Colin came down to the pool and enjoyed our antics. Another day he had the temperament and enthusiasm to swim with us in the rain – in the pool and in the sea. He was still moody and unpredictable at times – but much more of him was there – a real miracle again.

I was very thankful – it was wonderful. It was so difficult however, for I had spent the last six months preparing for the fact that he might not get any better, and now he was. I am bewildered – how am I to respond now? We get back home to Scotland – Colin still seems better – brighter, more himself. Still some seizures, but even in their midst better.

As time went on, I started to recognise new patterns. The good news was that the improvement in mood and thought process continued. Absolutely incredible. The bad news was that the seizure rate remained constant. Yet despite this, Colin continued to be more coherent and aware. The negative side of this, however, was that he became more frustrated as he was more aware of his condition. He felt useless that he couldn't drive, or earn a wage. He felt bad that he couldn't remember what to do in some situations, or whether he had seen a certain film, or what his pin number was.

I kept looking for help. Who could work with Colin to help him work all this out? Erskine didn't offer any form of help in the community – it could offer only respite – Colin found the information sheets I had asked for and was furious: why would he need respite? What would such a place offer him? Did I not want him – he felt suicidal. Combat Stress offered some help – but was it the right kind? In the past, contact with them had not been well received by Colin. Was his condition was not primarily PTSD orientated but rather epilepsy related? Was EMDR (Eye Movement Desensitising and Reprocessing) a possibility – but some web sites said it was contra-indicated for epilepsy.

I tried to think of a person who knew Colin or who might be able to work with him. He had become more lucid since the Upledger treatment – could someone work with him, to focus on the positive, on how to be a good husband and father, to focus on the things he *could* do. I phoned his neuro psychologist – and to my surprise she said I could come and see her.

I was hopeful she could offer some guidance, as to who would be the best person to work with Colin.

The interview did not work out like that! When I described Colin's symptoms – she said that she would not think it would be constructive for anyone to work with Colin at this point, as he would have problems remembering. She admitted it was a hellish existence for us and that was sad. Colin would not remember the sessions, they could stir up difficult issues for him and that would make life more difficult rather than to help him. She said it was me that needed help. Colin, she felt no-one could do anything for, not because they were unwilling, but because he was beyond help. I cried my way through most of this interview, and was left devastated. How could it possibly be wrong to ask for some support? If you had MS you would get some help, if you had Alzheimers you would get support. Why not with epilepsy? Are people with epilepsy less human and less worthy that everyone else? I was angry too, and didn't tell Colin about what had transpired. Later I spoke to her again, and she was very helpful and more positive, and spoke to Colin, but her assessment was again that he was deteriorating. She had known Colin for 14 years, and this was her area. She confirmed what I suspected, but it felt brutal. As for Colin, his condition gradually went back to where it had been before.

Chapter 9

POTHOLES, CRASHES, TRAUMA EVERYWHERE

'We have learned that trauma is not just an event that took place in the past. It is also the imprint left by that experience on the mind, brain and body. The imprint has ongoing consequence s for how the human organism manages to survive in the present. Trauma results in a fundamental reorganisation of the way the mind and brain manage perceptions. It changes not only how we think and what we think about but also our very capacity to think.'

'Being able to feel safe with other people is probably the single most important aspect of mental health: safe connections are fundamental to meaningful and satisfying lives.'

Bessel Van Der Kolk

Things were changing. Colin's trauma had already greatly impacted his perception of the world and his thought processes. Now as the realisation began to sink in, that Colin's seizures were actually damaging his brain, and that his brain function was becoming less clear, the cruelty of this diagnosis became more evident. Although Colin had worked so hard with his counsellor, and with different prayer partners over many years to try to come to terms with his experiences in combat, any progress he had made was gradually dissipated by the damage to his thought processes. The healing and processing that he had taken place, were undermined as his neurons failed to connect, and as he remembered less. He did not feel safe, but under threat. His past traumas and increasing damage combined to make him feel that many things were a threat – noises, words, faces, attitudes.

Colin became more irritable, and more unstable with each passing year. His earlier poems again illustrated some of the ongoing struggles he experienced in trying to integrate what had happened to him with his civilian life. They were emotional black holes which he kept falling into.

The first poems here, are about the internal battles he had – his seizured and traumatised brain was filled with self hatred about his own inability to function. The poem below was written after being unconscious for five days.

SO LONG ?

I'm losing on the swings,
I'm losing on the roundabouts.
Or have I already lost,
but won't get face the cost?

Playing the consequential game.
Had I lost it from the moment,
my fractured head became,
my very own enemy?

Oh yes, the six years,
Blood letting, scar inducing wars.
The six year 'Uni' fight,
discarded in just two nights.

One option, would seem kind.
An option's offer of a miracle,
chasing less, whilst losing more.

You've got to catch your dreams,
before they run away,
or lose your mind,

Oh yes, I could catch my dreams,
Oh yes, if one of my mental feet,
didn't nail me to the floor.

I'm still running around in circles.
Stumbling in blindness where once there was sight.
Face testing the woodwork, the white stick of night.

C.S. Gardner 87

BETRAYED

Oblivion's sunrise in thought,
betrayal of morning's delayed darkness.
A mind's butchered birth right of growth,
loss of sight via no understanding

'Cut out my eyes, for I can't see, 'though they still do',
Tools of life's trade lie useless in me.

One mental foot nails me to the floor,
running round in circles, missing the door.
Falling in blindness where once there was sight,
face testing the woodwork, the white stick of night.

The betrayal of mind's possible,
recognised agony of slow self destruct.
The slippery fragile hairline, death's option of release,
of life without mind, or mind without life.

Screaming in silence for help and understanding,
to a wall's gift of access to ignorance.
Blood from a self bitten hand runs in revenge,
for tears bought by another betrayal.

C.S. Gardner 1985

A STATE OF MIND

Screaming to the wallpaper,
my eyes flood with tears,
Screaming in silence,
for I don't want an event.
An event would bring ignorance,
ignorance means medicine,
more medicine,
less mind.

Quietly choking on saliva and nasal stream,
I thump my head, I beat my chair.
I stick pins in myself,
to create pain for myself,
which I hate most,
but want more.

I twist my face,
screwed agony of silence.
reaching out to the ceiling,
for a God, my last and only resolve.
I beg him, I curse him,
I curse him, I beg him.
Just one other could that could touch.
and for Christ's sake, why me ?

A week's slow self destruct,
of a mind's awareness.
Then the moment of dying;
gentle, without fear or pain.
A mind's last thought;
aware, but unfrightened,
Then five days of death,
for rebirth of life.

So think before you sit,
on your one eye of example,
that is your old age.
this was my youth,
my indelible imprint,
I shall carry to my grave.

C.S. Gardner 89 (from notes 84 – 87)

Colin lived with ambiguity every day. At times he was in touch with his rage and trauma, and his whole face would be black with depression and anger. Yet in other moods, his sense of humour came to the fore, and he could be very funny, with a very dry wit. In the midst of it all, Colin kept his faith in God. He believed that God would help him, he listened to praise music such as Matt Redmond, on good days he went to church. As he slowed down however, it became harder, as Colin felt that the organist was deliberately playing too quickly, and he couldn't keep up in his singing, and he became irritable.

Yet in the midst of that struggle there were moments of hope and colour. Colin often dreamt of God, and how God was with him, and these dreams brought him much consolation. Sometimes these dreams seemed quite euphoric in character, and sustained Colin for many days, reminding him that he was valued and loved.

One of Colin's earlier poems about a dream is on the next page . . .

A DREAM

I dreamed once of the gallant knight
Who'd battle alone against all odds
To set the wrongs of men to right
And fight for others to save their cause

I dreamed once of the hero of stories
Taunting danger for dramatic end
No deed impossible, hell hath no furore
To keep him from the Headline's dividend

I dreamed once of a lady's romance
Love born of lust for social rules
I saw reasons for weddings, logical dance
Yet none can mould life's jewels

I dreamed once of people dying in pain
Of what only man can do to man alone
The drummer's rhythm sounding blood red rain
To paint a scaffold built with human bone

I dreamed once of a man insane
Trapped within his mental cage
Chasing less by losing more for same
Certain death, the source of love and rage

I dreamed once of the love of Christ
A new life born, old sin washed away
The chance to quench a hidden thirst
To love a life and bless each day

I dream of an old head, now my last
Who lived each verse with heartfelt years
Then wrote each on the dew of grass
To remember them with morning's tears

C.S. Gardner August 89

Chapter 10

BEAUTIFUL PEOPLE ALONG THE WAY

'If you want a happy ending, that depends, of course, on where you stop your story.'

Orson Welles

'Can you feel my pain? Do you know my name?
Do you kneel and pray? Or do you walk away?'

Yvonne Lyons (from the song 'Again' in the album 'A Thousand Questions Why')

It was November 2007, and Colin found he had an abscess under his arm. It was so large that they had to operate under a general anaesthetic. This had happened before, and I knew it would need constant nursing care to change the bandages etc for days to come. He was in hospital, but he couldn't be taken for his procedure because there were emergencies that kept coming in. Eventually he had his operation, he didn't have a seizure and came back home. His wound healed well, and I was told that he was a good healer.

A week later, on a Friday, Colin started to tell me something bad had happened – he was not sure what it was – he asked me to tell him. When I took Colin to the nurse to get his dressing changed, his walking was really bad. He had poor balance, needed an arm to be able to get us the stairs. His agitation continued, and on Saturday, Colin was up till 4am pacing about – not easy to placate. He was up at 8am – asking what had happened. He was confused, and there was a slight drumming of fingers indicating seizure activity. I phoned the out of hours nurse and the doctor came out. Colin was standing out in hall standing with his head squint. He kept standing at funny angles, and looked a bit as if he was playing musical statues but without the music. Colin was quite tearful and felt he was going to die, that his brain was failing.

At Accident and Emergency, the movement got worse – his limbs also went now and again – legs and arms. The doctor wouldn't give him anything to damp down the movement, as it would mask the symptoms. She also wanted to wait to see how test results would come back, to see what they were dealing with. She failed to mention at that point that it would take four days for the urine result to come back. On the first ward, said they would probably keep him in and do for example a CAT scan*27 on Monday to see what was going on. I had to leave him there – confused and disorientated and with involuntary movements.

On Sunday when I went in his movement was less. He was still a bit confused, and his fingers were still a bit twitchy but less so, The staff helpfully told me that all tests etc were cancelled, as they had been in touch with neurology, and Colin was known to them and he had chronic epilepsy.

On Monday I told the registrar that I felt Colin still far from right – she agreed to listen and to keep Colin in longer if needed. In afternoon, Colin was chewing constantly with his mouth, different seizure activity! He had a seizure at 5.30pm and by evening he was, in bed, unresponsive.

On Tuesday afternoon, when I visited Colin was quite chatty – which is unusual after a seizure! He was very clean, and had had a shower. It occurred to me that Colin might be about to leave his passive phase and enter his combative phase, and I spoke to one of the staff nurses.

On Wednesday afternoon, Colin had his possessions all packed and ready to go, and he said he was getting out and coming home with me. I spoke to the nursing staff and they told me he had decided this, and they were waiting for me to come, so I could take him home. As the OT was still to come back, and the neurologists were to be asked for another opinion, I asked him to wait. It took the full visiting hour to convince Colin, as he very upset; he had had an encounter with a nurse who was getting him up that morning, and he wanted to leave. He was slightly manic – full of complaints – there was only one toilet, only one shower, a mark he didn't like on the floor, the place was not clean etc.

I phoned on the Thursday at 9.15am, the neurologists were happy with him, and I went to get him at 9.45am. Colin was confused, upset, desperate to get home: a mass of contradictions – thinking the nurses were out to get him, but wanting to give another nurse a cheque because she was retiring and wouldn't have a job. I spoke to the doctor and said that Colin was still acting out of character, and I was concerned about him. The doctor said there was nothing more he could do – Colin had difficult epilepsy – hard, but there it was. He was a young, earnest doctor, but ultimately reliant on the advice from the neurologists, who had been consulted by phone and not actually seen Colin. We were told to go home.

Later that day Colin seemed anxious. He told me that the face in the paper looked evil, that the nurses had been nasty to him – that they had turned off the light when he was in the shower. He said that the nurses were angry with him because of the incident with the day nurse, and that he had apologised to her, but that they were still coming after him, and he was afraid. He said that they woke him up too early, and made his life hard. He was frightened – then he said he had been attacked – that I had been attacked in the church. I said I would phone to see if I could get a doctor's appointment at the local GP's. He followed me up the stairs – he thought that I was in league with them and might betray him, that they might follow him to the house. I got a doctor's appointment for 4.50pm, and the GP said she would phone the hospital ward. I said that Colin was really confused, and that he was acting out of character – that he had also been like this in hospital. She phoned back to say that the ward have a different take – that he was in hospital because he had had two seizures, that they hadn't noticed any confusion, and that the only thing they had observed was that he didn't like taking instruction. They said he was orientated on discharge.

It was a very long afternoon – trying to reassure Colin, but not agitating him too much by saying that I did not agree fully with his story. He was on edge – afraid, worried, uncertain. I managed to get him to see the GP: she very calmly asked him lots of questions: what is your name, date of birth, the date (she actually got this wrong because it was wrong on the discharge certificate from the hospital). Who is the Prime Minister? Colin answered slowly, carefully, laboriously. The doctor turned to me and said that he seemed fine. I asked him to speak about the photo in the paper – he said it looked evil. I asked him if the nurses in the hospital had been ok, and he said they had attacked him. I reminded him that he said that I had been attacked in the church, and he said that this had happened. The doctor asked him how he knew this, but he could not reply. She took some blood tests, and got us to make an appointment in four days time, after the weekend. I asked for some temazepam to calm him down, if required, and she agreed, as he used to have it for this purpose. We went home. Colin took the temazepam and went to sleep. A few days later at home, he was calmer and seemed more in tune with the world.

The test results came back saying that Colin had a low sodium level, possibly caused by the tegretol. Talking to a friend, who had been reading on the internet, it appeared that low sodium could cause a lower seizure threshold and confusion. Over Christmas and the New Year, Colin was very sleepy – sleeping on many days till 1.30pm and 2.30pm. He was placid and quiet, and quite passive. On the 2nd of Jan, we went to the cinema, and had a pizza. As Colin was eating it, I thought – at least there is lots of salt in that. The next day he was up at 9am, played games outside with Andrew and got back to his chess board. He had not had a seizure since, was much more alert, more interested in life, up longer hours etc. Andrew and I wondered if daddy had been 'healed through pizza'. It was now the 8th January, and daddy was still well. Life is a mystery!

Later on, reflecting on Colin's behalf, I wrote a letter of complaint about his time in the hospital ward. It centred on how the hospital didn't really seem to be aware of Colin's cognitive condition, or to meet Colin's medical needs. The doctor on the ward wouldn't do an EEG to see how Colin really was, and if there was any unusual electric activity going on in his brain. I also commented that I thought it wasn't good practice that the neurologist did not actually come to the ward, but acted only on the observations of the medical staff on the phone. Another point was that Colin was discharged in a poor mental state, and this was not noticed. The reply admitted nothing, and said they thought the standard of care was good. We got an appointment with the consultant in the new year, and a follow up one in the autumn.

Taking Colin to doctor's appointments often seemed a tedious process, but it was lightened by the porters who told jokes, and the nurses who would treat you as human beings and have a laugh. Colin loved wearing interesting tee shirts too, that said things like 'I bet you don't recognise me without my cape' and 'saving energy 24/7' – they always brought a smile to everyone's face.

A Topsy Turvy Day

The carer came in the door. He had established a good rapport with Colin, and most weeks they would go out for lunch together. Colin loves his food – perhaps that is one of the things he is most consistent in. A 'big breakfast' is acceptable any time of the day or night. This Friday however, Colin had had a seizure, 36 hours before, and he was a bit groggy. The carer – we'll call him Gerard, had something to drink and chatted with Colin. The usual banter went on. The Disability Living Allowance doctor had just been in to do an assessment, and Colin was exhausted from 2 hours of talk and examination. A little later I came back after having picked up Andrew from school, and Gerard was bantering away, but somehow Gerard seemed a bit off . . . a bit different, and I asked him if he was ok. He said he was fine, but his eyes seemed a bit all over the place, and he started to babble. Then he said he was really tired, and he put his head on the table and went to sleep.

I knew Gerard was a diabetic, but I had never seen a hypo before. I phoned his boss, and he said give him something sweet to drink, and he should just come out of it. I had some fruit juice. When I spoke to Gerard he was responsive, and took some juice, but nothing seemed to change. Every five minutes or so, I kept talking to him to check he was responsive. He told me he was fine, just tired. I asked him if he had his trademark bottle of coke in the car – he said no. He still wasn't coming out of it, so I phoned his boss again. He said if I could get some coke, that would be better. I went out and got some. Gerard was still responsive, but not keen on drinking. Colin was sitting opposite Gerard in all of this. He looked at him quizzically, as if to say, how could you fall asleep in my company?

Gerard was still not responding, so I phoned his boss again. He said I should phone an ambulance, which I did. I told Andrew that there could be some ambulance men coming as the carer wasn't feeling very well. He watched tv, and said ok. The phone kept going, and I wasn't sure who it was, so I kept picking it up. It was work calls, about meetings and paperwork. I said I would phone back (someone later said I sounded a bit stressed). I kept thinking it is epilepsy I deal with, not hypos – this is not my area.

After another five minutes, Gerard started to come round. He raised his head, put on his glasses and had some more coke. He gazed round at us and looked at his watch. It was after 5pm. He looked at us again. He noticed how soaked with sweat he was, and how cold he felt. The doorbell went, and the ambulance people came in. They were good, and saw Gerard was better. They tested his blood sugar, and chatted to him about his diet, recommending he go to the doctor. They asked him if he lived here. We said no. They asked what he was doing here, and Gerard had to say he was my husband's carer. Everyone started to smile, and then to laugh, as the craziness of the situation started to hit home. Who exactly was caring for who here? Is being supported by carers always this complex? How could the carer end up with a hypo, and we end up caring for him? Life is never straightforward. After some more banter, Gerard signed the disclaimer, and the ambulance crew left.

I told Andrew that Gerard was better now. He had missed it all watching tv. Gerard had some toast and some more coke. He changed his shirt, and started to feel better. Eventually he went home. People on the phone asked me how I was, I said fine. Who could explain all of this?

The summer went reasonably well. The greatest blessing was getting back to Florida. Colin had a seizure the night before we flew, and was really poorly. He was very brave and managed to get on the plane, even though it was delayed 30 minutes. That doesn't sound much, but it was 30 minutes extra to stand in the lobby waiting. If Colin had sat down, he would have gone to sleep. So we had to stay upright. Our flight gate was closed, and every now and again Colin would suggest he was going to go through the other flight gate as it was open. I had to try and explain that each different gate lead to a different plane and destination, but he just thought it would be quicker, and would save us standing there!

On the flight, I told the cabin staff that Colin had had a seizure recently and wasn't feeling too good, and they just left him alone. The only hard bit was that he didn't put the lock on the toilet door when he went, but I just stood nearby and formed a queue, so no-one else tried to get in. The other slightly hairy bit, was arriving at Sanford, and the American security official asking for Colin's right and left index fingers for prints. Colin had no idea what he meant, and it took ages to sort out. The official got quite impatient, till I explained he was not well, and he said he could see that. I asked the Border guard to slow down, and we managed to muddle our way through and get into the country. We had come thousands of miles in the plane, but getting these last few feet across the line at the airport was by far the most difficult bit.

The holiday went as well as it could have. We saw a couple of theme parks – slowly and painstakingly! We found a ride that we could all go on, and we all had our picture taken. We stayed for a while with our lovely friends, who were so patient and kind with us. Colin had another seizure, and was slow and a bit moody. We went for more prayer, which as always helped. Colin quietened and became a bit more relaxed. I just felt tired, but I got some rest, and that was great. One beautiful day, we all went swimming in the pool, and it was wonderful. Colin and Andrew played throw and catch with a ball in the pool in the warm sunshine, and it was relaxed and great fun. A fantastic memory.

Another very moving memory was going to see Shamu at Seaworld Orlando. Colin often responded well to animals and mammals – some deep instinct being engaged, which brought him peace. There are many arguments around the keeping of such whales in such an environment, but we just enjoyed seeing the whale and its graceful and powerful movements through the water. Colin was mesmerised, and Andrew and I were just grateful that he could focus on such a magnificent creature. At the end of the show, the announcer made an announcement that all veterans should stand up, and be acknowledged for their service. We were astounded – no one in the UK had ever said this. Colin and a number of others stood up, and everyone clapped him. Hot tears rolled down my face, as it was one of the only public acts of acknowledgement that he had ever had. And we had to travel to Orlando to receive it!

On our return, we had an appointment with the consultant. We hoped for nothing. The letter of complaint we had put in regarding Colin not receiving adequate treatment in hospital had elicited a response. The letter said this appointment was for the consultant to 'reassure us'. It was not a promising beginning. Colin had had a seizure that day, after a period of about 11 days without one. We waited in the waiting room – it was mobbed with lots of others waiting also. Families with young children, older parents with their son, a middle aged couple. It was a long time for Colin to sit and wait. When we went in, the consultant looked through the file, and asked to be reminded of the background. I gave him the last letter from the hospital in response to my letter complaint. He read it, saying he remembered. Discussion took place, where he said that he felt sorry for the people on the wards trying to deal with all of this, and not having time to get to know the patient in more detail. He reckoned I had made my point by complaining, and that there was not much to be gained by taking it further.

A Week in the Life of Colin – October 2008

For some unknown reason yet again, Colin was having a bad month. He was quite well when we went to Millport in September for the weekend, and that was lovely, a really good experience. However his seizure rate was not so good again, and the thing was, that even 5/6 days after a seizure he was still very sleepy and slow and bad tempered. On Monday, he had a seizure in the morning, and I managed to give him a new after seizure medication. Colin slept all afternoon, and I wondered if he had had another seizure later, for after he tried to stand up he kept falling over. It was as if his balance had gone completely. I managed to give him a shower, but he had a little dinner and then slept again till bedtime.

On Tuesday, he was still quite poor. He woke up at lunchtime, and spent the day with his mum and dad. He seemed a little perkier by evening. The next day I took Andrew and the dog to see a friend, knowing that the carer would be in to see Colin at lunch time. When we returned, I said to Colin that I would make some tea, and found that the fridge and freezer were full of fish! Apparently 28 trays of fish, costing £380, which Colin had bought at the door. A man came round and tried to persuade Colin to buy it. He wanted cash, and helped Colin count it out from his wallet. Colin paid partly by cash and partly by cheque.

The next day I called the police, and they logged it as an incident. We cancelled the cheque with the bank. I found the next door neighbour had also bought fish, and he gave the name and address of the firm. I phoned up, and made a strong complaint, only to be told it wasn't them – it was a different company as they only sold frozen fish, and it was correctly packaged. However they would be interested in helping us out, as their business had suffered, as many people on the doorsteps didn't want to buy fish, as they said someone else had been round, and had been quite aggressive. The next day, a man from that company came round, and said that he had another client with a similar story to ourselves, and that he would put us in touch with her, so it would help us to have more of a case to go to Trading Standards with. I also inspected an old tray of fish from a previous occasion, and found another name and address! This too needed to be fed into the system.

However it was a hard week. I was meant to be having some time off to study, and instead all I seemed to deal with were calls about fish! For Colin the whole experience was humiliating and embarrassing. He was trying to do something nice – to buy some fish for me! Instead it all blew up in his face, and made him feel worse. Colin was vulnerable to people coming round the doors – on occasion he gave people his credit or debit card, so they could get him money from the bank. It is so sad when people are taken advantage of in their own homes, and can't even open the door without being exploited! It seems that nowhere is safe, and legislation to make things better is not easy to enact effectively.

Encounters with 'Helpful' People – 2008-9

When you are trying to support someone who is chronically sick, you meet so many different people along the road. Many are reasonably helpful, others are wonderful, and some are dire.

Colin had been seeing a cranial-osteopath Anna Potter for about four months. She had been recommended, and we were open to what she might manage to accomplish. The theory here, as at the Upledger, was that a gentle massage of Colin's spine and cranium could relieve the build up of pressure and smooth out any kinks and knots in his neck and spine, and that this should cause his whole metabolism to function to work better. She came every two weeks, and was from a hospital background. She was easy to talk to, liked dogs (very useful), visited at home, and believed she could help to reduce Colin's seizure rate. She was consistent, and listened well. It was early days, but for a while Colin seemed to be having slightly fewer seizures – four a month. He also seemed to be less sleepy and slow in between times. It sounded wonderful – worth celebrating!

And yet, what also came across was the amount of brain damage which had been taking place. Colin was still very quiet at times. A couple of times he tried the nonagram in the paper, and worked on it for three or four hours without stopping. He maybe got ten words, and three of them didn't count as they didn't have the right letters. Colin wanted to do more, to go out and meet people, but if they do not listen to him and make a fuss of him, then he quickly loses interest. He laughs at jokes which he may not understand, and can seem quite genial. What he really makes of what is going on however, I don't know.

The other day I was hoping to go into town for a few hours by myself to go into the sales. I was really looking forward to it. I gave Colin his tablets, and my mum was looking after Andrew. Colin decided that he wanted to come, and he came out with me. He had been in such a rush however, he didn't take his tablets, and therefore had two seizures that night. He was so ill afterwards, so sleepy and just walking aimlessly round the house – I had to lock the front door just in case he had a notion to go out. I had given him his after-seizure medication, but he had spat it out. Colin had another seizure 4 days later – virtually unheard of, for normally there would be a much longer spell between a double seizure and a single. He was very poorly all over again. This morning he got up and had breakfast about 10am, and then went back to sleep. It is 2.30pm and he is still asleep! In the end, we stopped the osteopathy; like everything else, it seemed to make a difference for a short time, and then everything reverted back to type.

The question for any carer is how do I support someone through their situation effectively? I could wake Colin up when he sleeps so much, but that would make him more grumpy, and he would just sleep again in the chair. When he has a cluster of seizures, Colin is so poorly for days on end. And when he is getting better, he is often restless at night, e.g. starts shaving at 1am in the morning and waking everyone up. Yet he has no idea that this is not one of his better ideas. In a way, we really want to encourage him to shave, so you don't want to put him off – just because it is the middle of the night. It is one of the many ways our family life has become so strange – we encourage things that look ridiculous, because that is the best option we have.

Another person we have met in the last few months, is a neuro-psychiatrist, a Dr Duffy, who specialises in working with patients with physical disabilities and illnesses. We went to see him, not really knowing what to expect. The epilepsy consultant had said that he was referring Colin to see if he could recommend a drug to help Colin's post-ictal symptoms and/or a drug to deal with the psychotic episodes.

Our first impression was of a man who spoke fast, but listened well, and wanted to hear our story. We told it yet again. He asked more questions. He used the term 'brain injury' – and I reacted in my customary way: how do you define that etc, as Colin has epilepsy. As a doctor he was excellent, for he listened to my concerns about Colin and his episodes of being detached from reality, and he said calmly and in a matter of fact way, 'That can happen after seizures – that is a description of disordered brain function'. We related other incidents from over the years – Colin's ability to play what looked like musical statues (a catatonic state the doctor called it), his idea that his body was not really his own and that parts had been replaced by a robot etc. The psychiatrist said this was all consistent with disordered brain function after a seizure – he talked of it as if it were an every day event. After seven and a half years, this was the first person we had ever spoken to who seemed to understand what we were describing, and to be remotely sympathetic; he took the time to explain what we had been seeing. It made a huge difference, for the first time to actually understand what Colin was going through.

Lorazepam*[28] was the drug to be given if these symptoms were shown, and he recommended it after a seizure, and if Colin was becoming agitated or distressed. He also sensibly said that he would not recommend an anti-psychotic drug, as it would just lower Colin's seizure threshold, and this would not be helpful. At the end of it all, he said he would like to look over Colin's file again, and to see us for another appointment. We were impressed – as he didn't just fob us off, or send us away, but spoke knowledgably and with insight, and seemed to want to know more about Colin's condition. How wonderful!

Realising anew the extent of the damage to Colin's brain, I tried to get some more support in place. I spoke to a really nice man from Headway, who said they would be willing for Colin to come along to a meeting, even though his case was more unusual. I would need to get a carer to go with him, even if he chose to go only when he felt up to it. It was looking rather too complicated, as Colin finds it hard to relate to other people with brain injuries. I phoned an organisation we had been recommended to go to, and they said they would send someone out that week to do an assessment visit. They didn't phone back till seven days later, when they said the boss had been off, but they would now plan the visit, and give me a time and date. The next day they phoned back to say that they were now full, and not taking on any more clients. What a waste of time and energy.

By the end of the year, I was feeling a bit weary. Colin seemed so damaged that I didn't know what would help him. It felt like the whole year had been spent in appointments and doctors and trying to access different services. I phoned the social worker, as we had asked for an occupational therapist for Colin, and she confirmed that he had been on the waiting list for a year, but no OT was yet forthcoming.

Andrew sat at the breakfast table the other morning, and he said the words, 'No offence, but sometimes I feel as if I don't have a dad'. I said I understood, and I said that I wanted him to tell me how he felt. I said because Colin's brain doesn't always work properly, it can feel as if he is not really there, although his body is present, his personality often seems diluted so such an extent that he does not seem to be present. Instead there is a caricature – a person who doesn't want you to be noisy or to ask him anything, yet wants to be included and be appreciated.

In the midst of my doom and gloom, I loaded photos from my digital camera onto my computer, something which I had meant to get round to for a year and a half. The way my laptop works, it uses a random selection of these pictures for my screensaver, and this was actually a real blessing and turn around for me. For on the screen appeared all these pictures – holidays, birthdays, friends, days out, landscapes, flowers – all the things which had happened over the last year, moments in time which had been good, worth celebrating. And it helped me get a healthier perspective on the last year, a balance.

I remember reading Wordsworth's *The Prelude*, and what he said about 'spots of time':

'There are in our existence spots of time
That with distinct pre-eminence retain
A renovating virtue, whence . . . our minds
Are nourished and invisible repaired.'

Remembrances of good times shared together somehow made the bad ones more bearable, and brought a sense of healing and restoration.

COLIN'S CHARCOAL DRAWING OF 'CONFLICT'

Chapter 11

SOME LIGHT RELIEF FROM THE PAST

Colin remembered incidents from his military days – not just tragic ones, but ones that were embarrassing and even had a humorous side. Serving in the military was not always straightforward: what happened to him when he got shot, was a case in point.

At some stage of the Northern Ireland troubles, there was a flare up in Belfast between the two religious communities of such vehemence that outbreaks of mass violence were considered distinctly possible. Additional permanently manned patrol points were established at community boundaries; metal sheeting was used to build high walls in areas previously 'calm' to prevent the daily throwing of missiles; requests has been made for all available Police and Security Forces personnel to be temporarily seconded to Belfast. The combination of some recent inflammatory events and shortly to be 'celebrated' rituals of military/political/religious dates, with parades viewed by each side as blatant displays of insult, the authorities were worried about a flare up of previously unexperienced proportions.

It was after 11.00pm and we'd been driving around the streets since 8.00pm. Routine patrol duties, checks of suspicious cars, groupings of people and the like. We weren't there in any 'Crime Squad' capacity, just to swell numbers and the overall area coverage. The night was very dark due to the sky's heavy cloud and would likely mean rain before long.

Most of the pubs had closed but there were still a few 'Chinese' and Fish and Chip shops open, which we were currently appreciating. Ryan was in the back seat calming his stage of starvation with two steak pie suppers and a single sausage. Boris was driving, picking at his chicken supper which I was holding in my right hand, whilst I ate my own steak pie supper from my lap with my left hand. So far the evening had been quiet, so we stopped to wash the meal down with cans of coke-cola or whatever. When finished we collected all the rubbish into a carrier bag and stuffed it under one of the seats.

We were studying our allotted area of patrol, deciding what we should do next, when a radio request for an available unit in our area was made. I looked to Boris, who nodded, and I responded to the call:

'Hello Papa Delta, this is Charlie Sierra responding your request, over.'

'Roger Charlie Sierra, response acknowledged, can you hold, over?'

'Roger, Papa Delta, Charlie Sierra positive, out'.

With the pause we fully opened our area map and co-ordinated our position with key points of reference. After a period of radio chat, we were contacted again.

'Hello Charlie Sierra, this is Papa Delta, over'.

'Roger Papa Delta, over'.

'Charlie Sierra, we have a report of a 'two seven' (prowler) in back gardens of Steven Street, Auldhouse Road. If you are insufficient or unfamiliar with site, we have Sierra Foxtrot (security forces) unit on standby, over'.

'Roger Papa Delta, Charlie Sierra is sufficient and has Sierra Foxtrot member familiar with site, over'.

'Roger Charlie Sierra, Sierra Foxtrot unit will remain in area for your assistance, over'.

'Roger Papa Delta, Charlie Sierra, out'.

The security forces member meant myself, who had patrolled this area as a uniformed soldier during my first six months. As we drove towards the site, I described the back gardens with as much details as I could remember. The type of garden layout, the height of the walls and their overall state of maintenance.

We decided to clear each side of gardens individually, moving from one to another in a leapfrog fashion of two cover, one moves. Due to my familiarity with the area it was decided I should go first and try to open one of the garden gates. The decision was perfectly correct, but I wasn't going to let them off that easily.

'Why am I on my own opening the gate?' I asked.

'You're the professional soldier,' Ryan replied 'And you've got those certificates of marksmanship that you keep telling us about.'

'So what? I'm still not bullet proof.'

Then Boris argued, 'But you're the smallest target and you've got the biggest gun.'

Raising myself in my seat, I said, 'And I bet I've got the biggest something else too'. With a series of slaps around the head from maps, I was told, 'Sit down for Chrissakes. You don't always have to act like a policeman!'

Approaching our site, we tossed the remains of our cigarettes out the windows. Just before the end of the street, Ivan switched the car headlights and engine off, letting us coast silently around the corner to within a few car lengths of the buildings we waited. We cocked our guns in the car but left the safety catches off. A blatant disregard of normal firearms procedure but in this kind of situation if a bullet was fired at you, there'd be less than a third of a second to respond before the next one probably hit you. Insufficient time to prepare one's weapons for firing. We buttoned our jackets to avoid loose material catching on things and turned the collars up in order to keep as dark a shape as possible. A shirt and tie was hardly the best apparel for creeping about in the night.

Then climbing out, we silently closed the doors of the car and moved to the end of the lane between our gardens and buildings. We started to creep up the lane at the low crouch, and at the start of the first garden, we paused to study the overall area, although with so many plants and bushes, it was hard to discern any one feature.

A prowler could mean almost anything. Considering the tension in the City, it may have meant a gunman, someone preparing to put a 'Molotov Cocktail' or a brick with a bag full of shit through someone's window; perhaps an 'honest' burglar or maybe even someone stealing women's underwear off the washing line. Whatever, someone had made the report and someone had to check it out.

A while later, after each of us shook his head to the others to indicate nothing suspicions, Boris and Ryan changed their positions to give me cover whilst I moved towards the nearest garden gate. After fiddling mentally and physically with the lock, the gate opened and I pushed it gently ajar, praying that the hinges wouldn't grate or squeak. With a minimum of noise, I managed to push the gate sufficiently open for me to squeeze inside. Once in the garden, I carefully checked around me and moved to a position with the wall of the house behind me so as to cover for Boris and Ryan.

After a short pause, I indicated to the others and Ryan crept into the garden, then across to the separating wall. With some hesitation, Ryan tried to check the other side of the wall and then scrambled over. I indicated to Boris who entered the garden, paused to close the gate, and then followed Ryan. After the next garden was cleared, Boris indicated to me to come over. At a very low crouch, I moved forward carefully, trying not to make any noise with my footsteps, using every little piece of plant cover the garden could offer. I tried to keep myself calm so that I could breathe as silently as possible and crept up to the wall.

Once there, I positioned myself in the classic 'low profile' setting as per combat training. This was lying stretched on the top of the wall supported by your left arm and right leg. Then by moving your left leg and body under your support you move over the wall keeping the lowest possible profile yet at all times holding the gun in your right hand ready for use. When over, I took up a position similar to previous gardens in order to cover for Boris and Ryan. We repeated this system a number of times, but sometimes having to adjust it; with a lighted window where the curtains weren't drawn, we had to almost crawl flat against the wall of the house underneath the window.

When most of the gardens had been cleared, I was crouching in one providing cover for the others but starting to feel strained and tired. With a simultaneous deafening bang, a powerful and painful smack on my backside, I catapulted myself into the bush I'd been crouching behind with a cry.

Anyway, I was now entangled in the middle of a bush with prickly thorns scratching my face and hands as I tried to move. I wasn't even sure which way up I was. My backside felt as if it was being rubbed and pressed all over but was growing increasingly numb. I heard Boris and Ryan shouting:

'Police! Freeze!'

'Police! Put down your weapon!! Already totally confused with my position, the voices I could hear weren't providing any clarity. I heard Ryan shout:

'Don't do anything, we are the Police!' Then the woman replied, 'How do I know you're the bloody Police?'

By now I could make out the figures of Boris and Ryan standing on the lawn to my side. Ryan stepped towards the voice holding up his warrant card.

'One step more and you're deid!' she screeched.

'Look at my warrant card', Ryan appealed. 'It says Police'.

'Ah canna see it from here'.

Ryan hesitated for a minute, his eyes furtively flicking over the woman. Then with outstretched arms, he slowly crouched down on the lawn and placed his handgun onto the ground. Then equally slowly, he stood up, brought his outstretched arm with the card around to the front and moved very gradually towards her. For every inch of Ryan's approach, the woman kept her double-barrelled shotgun pointing directly at his body.

I was still entangled in the bush, but had decided in the best interests of all concerned, especially my own, to remain frozen and not attract any attention.

Ryan advanced to the stage where his stomach was practically pressing against the ends of the shotgun's barrels.

'Careful now', she warned.

'I'm trying to be', he replied. Ryan's card was now about six inches from her face and she was screwing up her eyes, moving her chin forward, in an effort to focus on the print. After some scrutiny, she relaxed her face and said:

'Alright, I believe youse'. However, she still kept the shotgun pointing at Ryan's stomach. He asked her hesitatingly:

'Could you then, please put your gun down?'

'Aye, okay', she replied and did so.

Ryan took the shotgun from her and unloaded it. By now practically every window overlooking the gardens was alight, with curious and very entertained faces peering out. Moving to stand in the light from one of the, Boris called out a couple of times:

'It's okay everyone, we are the Police. There's no problem. Just a small accident.'

Reassured or not, the residents were obviously fascinated with the show, especially the figure half buried in the bush with his backside hanging out. They just continued to watch the proceedings and nobody went back inside or closed their curtains.

Ryan was talking to the woman asking her various questions. I could see Boris moving across to me, presumably to help me get out of the bush. As he squatted beside me he asked:

'Are you alright Colin?'

'How should I know?' I retorted. To which Boris forcefully answered:

'Colin! Be serious! Do you know where you were hit?'

I'd been feeling tired and strained before, now I was furious at the events, especially my personal circumstances and did not want to add to my humiliation by acceding to an order of discipline from any other bastard. Working hard to control the immediate retort I wished to give, I forced myself to recognise the legitimacy of Boris's order and quietly replied:

'Okay, sorry Boris.'

'Doesn't matter under these conditions Colin, but what can you actually feel?'

'I'm not sure. The top half of me seems normal, but my arse feels dead and my legs are starting to go a bit funny. What can you see?' After a pause for examination, he answered:

'Going by the state of your jacket and trousers, it looks like you only caught the edge of what I think was grouse shot, most of which went into the ground. You can thank your lucky stars you were wearing a leather jacket, it seems to have absorbed most of the impact, but you'll still need a new pair of trousers'.

'Can I claim those on expenses?'

'Don't worry, we'll find you some way.' He chuckled. 'I can't find any blood on your shirt so you seem to be okay. I didn't want to start moving you until I was sure there wasn't a more serious wound, but I think we can get you out now.'

With Boris pulling back various branches, I managed to disentangle myself from the bush. Now on the lawn, lying on my side, I moved to try and stand up but my legs wouldn't co-operate. There was pain in my right ankle as I stood up on it, but as I tried to shift my weight to the left foot, I fell over because my leg wasn't responding as quickly as I would wish. I explained the problem to Boris who indicated that Ryan was just about finished with the old woman and would soon be able to help us. Looking at my right ankle I could see I'd caught some of the shot just above the edge of my shoe. The sock was a bit bloody and any probing of the ankle was painful, but at least it wasn't numb. Either way, I suppose it was better than no ankle at all, or even no Colin.

I could see Ryan folding his notebook and putting his pen away. Then he accompanied the old woman over to her door and took her back into the house. Returning holding a box of shotgun cartridges, Ryan walked over to us picking up the shotgun and his hand gun on the way. When all together, Boris and Ryan helped me stand up with my arms over their shoulders. With a slow swing of the left leg and a painful limp on the right ankle, we made gradual progress back to the car.

'Maybe this wasn't such a great idea after all.' I said through a contorted grin of clenched teeth.

'Aye, one of the army units would've been a better match for her,' Boris said.

'He is an army unit though,' said Ryan. At which point we started to laugh, fuelled by the relief of finally leaving the gardens. But trying to sound as tired as possible, I added:

'That was not quite my meaning, chaps.'

'What?'

'I meant, the more of this walking I do, the more painful my arse becomes.' Laughing quite loudly, Boris said:

'Irrefutable proof that there is life after death!'

'Aye, but at which end? I didn't even know she was there'.

'Ah, don't worry about that', replied Ryan. 'According to what she told me, she was already standing behind the door, with it just a small fraction ajar looking out. As soon as she saw your shape taking cover behind the bush, she was able to open the door further, without the noise of handles or locks and step out barefoot and shoot you'.

'Very professional,' I muttered. Then it clicked. 'You mean she was ready with that shotgun even before we arrived?'

'Apparently so, she put in the original report.'

'But she's half bloody blind!', I exclaimed.

'Aye, sort of. She says she can distinguish most things, but precise lines are blurred, and with printed letters, she can only make out something really close'.

Swearing a bit at how 'lucky' I was, we reached the car. I balanced on Ryan as Boris went around opening the doors. Then with both of them grinning in obvious sympathy, they asked if I could rather sit or kneel on the back seat. Considering how much life had already been restored to me, I opted for the latter. Once inside, Ryan called in over the radio to report the suspect site had been cleared, but added there had been an accidental discharge, in case of other reports of a gunshot. He stated the unit would be standing down in order to take a member injured in an accident to hospital.

On the drive to the hospital, Ryan informed us as to the old woman's history. She'd worked a fairly small farm with her husband for most of their lives. Not particularly profitable, they had to sell off various parts over the years. Then with their grown up children moving on to start their own lives and families, they continued to work the farm, but less and less with each advancing year. When her husband eventually died, she sold what little was left of the farm and moved into town in order to be closer to shops, social services, hospitals, etc. The shotgun had always been on the farm, so when finally moving, she just brought it with her because she'd be on her own.

Ryan was thoughtfully chewing at the end of his thumbnail when he turned to me.

'Colin, I was thinking. There was nothing malicious about her actions tonight. I don't think the shotgun has ever been licensed, although we have it now and the same thing could never happen again. But rather than give her any unnecessary hassle, what say you we forget about this and just leave it unofficial?'

'That's fine by me Ryan, but just so long as you can get me some anaesthetic soon. No joking guys, this is starting to get fuckin' painful.' At that point, I could feel the car gaining speed as Boris pressed heavily onto the accelerator.

When at the hospital, being helped out of the car by Boris and Ryan, it became evident that my left leg was again functioning normally. My right ankle hurt even more as I tried to walk and every leg movement caused intense pain in my buttocks. But once inside the building, the staff quickly produced a trolley bed. When I'd passed by jacket and shoulder holster to Boris, I was helped to climb up onto the bed. I was taken to a small, well lit room with bottles, trays full of instruments, bundles of cotton wool, bandages and the like. The nurses stripped me naked, pushed a pillow under my hips so I was lying front down raised on my elbows, whilst they set about preparing me. I tried to briefly explain the night's circumstances, and heard some tightly controlled sounds of laughter.

One of the nurses cane around to my face and started to wipe over the scratches from the bush. I could hear the others collecting bits and pieces together before leaving the room.

'You've got an awful lot of scratches here,' she said.

'I didn't know how many I had.'

'Aye, sort of like a railway junction. But don't worry, there's nothing that won't heal in a day or two. You'll keep your good looks.'

'Does that mean you think I look handsome?' I asked. She studied my face, hesitantly.

'Aye, I'd give you handsome.'

'Thanks', I said. 'I was needing reassurance about something.'

I lay there for a while, studying the blank walls and the various fitments, until the nurses plus a doctor returned. They quickly set to work and we exchanged conversation on the night's events. The doctor explained the type of repairs he would perform on me, and I was assured that despite a couple of stitches here and there, I'd be free of any scar tissue. Even as he said so, the thought had occurred to me that it was hardly an area I would wish to expose to frequent scrutiny.

Whilst the doctor was working, I'd heard the door open and shut several times with the nurses. I was not aware of any additional presence until I heard a voice say:

'My, what luscious pink cheeks you have Colin.'

'Boris?' I stretched my head around to see Boris and Ryan bending over studying my buttocks.

'Oh God,' I groaned.

Not long after that, with a considerable number of small elastoplast bandages stuck on me, I was given instructions to avoid sitting on any hard surfaces for a few days and allowed to leave with the others. We returned to the barracks and on the doctor's recommendation, I took the next day off, spending most of it in my room lying front down on the bed doing some collation work with information notes, reading a book or looking at mainly blank walls and windows with the glass painted over.

The following day, I was back at work although mainly restricted to office duties. As I had expected I was greeted with plentiful quantities of grins and comments. Nor did it take me too long to realise that a rendition of the events had spread like wild fire across the intelligence network. Telephone communications various from the seemingly normal, interspersed with remarks like:

'I hope this isn't becoming too tiresome for you, please feel free to sit down if you wish.'

Others opened in a blatantly direct fashion with remarks such as:

'Is that Colin?'

'Yes.'

'How's your bum feeling today?'

Although my new fame became somewhat of an irritation at times, the final testing moment in a speedy recovery arose with the removal of the elastoplast. A rather hairy person by birthright, it proved to be a source of unexpected additional pain, just when I thought it was all over.

On a good day, Colin will refer to incidents like this, and laugh about them – in retrospect. On a bad day, the day seems to consist of waiting for Colin to come round, of coaxing him into the shower, of doing lots of washings. Sometimes we just need to let him be alone, for he cannot cope with any people or any questions. Cups of tea are put down in front of him, and he drinks them when he is ready – two hours later. Life consists of going from the bedroom, to the bathroom, to the tv room and back. The cushions on the couch have a permanent indentation in them, as Colin can sit there for so long. What kind of life is this?

Colin wrote about how he felt:

What, who am I? Am I so different from all these others? Is it my past, the experiences of the past? The experiences of my injuries, my attempts to overcome their results, or a combination of them both. To explain my 'strange' behaviour to people, to people so different in all respects that they could not possibly ever have any comprehension of my experiences, or me – must I resort to the whole 'life story' With no possibility of understanding from anyone, must I always resort to a fawning attempt at sympathy, however disguised it may be?

Whilst on active service, there was nothing CSG couldn't do, and proved it. But look at me now . . . a fraction of what I used to be, far behind my friends great and small. I feel so alone, so isolated. Instead of building on my age, expanding as others have done, I have shrunk.

Chapter 12

GOING ROUND IN CIRCLES

'The best portions of a good man's life are his little, unremembered acts of kindness and of love.'

William Wordsworth

Time passes. In some way it seems as if life is normal. It seems so for us, and yet there is this discordant quality throughout. We all go round the house on tiptoe trying not to make a noise that will wake daddy.

We make the most of good days, when things seem better. We maybe go on a visit to the shops, or for a de-caffeinated coffee. Water pistol fights are a favourite – Colin and Andrew excel at these, especially on a warm day, although any day will do! I try to encourage water pistol fights to happen outside, it helps.

Another series of circular events

It was four weeks before we were due to go on holiday. On the Sunday, Colin said that he had a bit of a sore shoulder, and it looked a bit purple. He felt a bit sick and had a seizure the next day. He slept for most of the Monday – this was not uncharacteristic. It was a holiday Monday, so I waited till Tuesday to go to make an appointment, and got one for the afternoon. The GP looked at Colin's back and confirmed it was a sebaceous cyst, and would need to be excised. It was too big for her to do at the surgery; he would have to go to A and E.

This was beginning to seem horribly familiar. We went to A and E, and it was very busy. The day after a Bank holiday is always busy apparently. I asked if it was better to come on the bank holiday itself, but no, the nurse said that was busy too! We waited to see the surgeon. He seemed like he was Italian – very young and handsome and with a charming manner.

He and his paduan (not the right term – we'd been watching too much Star Wars) measured the cyst and looked at it, and said it was hospital policy to usually do a general anaesthetic for this kind. I said that Colin had six tonic clonic seizures a month. And that I would rather he didn't have a general anaesthetic in case it interfered with his anti-convulsants. To my amazement, after consultation he agreed, and they carried out the procedure in the cubicle bed. I was just a few feet away through the curtain, and I felt sick just listening, especially when all the stuff – and I mean all of it – from the cyst ended up on the floor not far from me. Colin said he felt it a bit, but he was very brave – he always had a high tolerance for pain. I was to make an appointment with the nurse, to get the wound packed the next day. Colin seemed fine. He liked the idea that at last he was in a situation where his bravery was recognised!

I took him to the practice nurse the next day, and remembered to give him his two paracetamol an hour before his visit. She could see how deep the wound was, and she called the doctor in, as she thought that there was a slight infection in the wound. It was Colin's GP who came in – and I was horribly conscious that I had just put in the request for Colin's 'fit to fly' letter. He prescribed antibiotics. At lunch time, Colin said he felt he was slowing down. He felt strange sensations in his limbs, he became a bit emotional and there seemed a slight repetition in his hand movements. He thought there was something seriously wrong, but didn't know what it was.

It was the surgery's half day, but I just caught them. Having been there only two hours before, it seemed a bit silly to be calling again, and the doctor on call was to phone back. It was the GP in the practice whom we didn't know. She was exceptionally nice. I explained my concerns, and said it could just be nothing, and she said but you are worried because I hear it in your voice. That was quite an extra-ordinary insight. She said she was on till 6pm, and to see how things went, and to phone back if I was concerned. I waited for another couple of hours, but Colin said he felt worse, and he seemed a bit more agitated. I phoned back, and the GP asked me to bring him in. We sat and she went through many questions – in a very person centred and natural way. She outlined our options, and asked what we thought. At first I thought, I don't want to bother people – maybe he will just get better. Yet on the other hand, she said that she had worked in hospitals before, and she knew how to involve the neurologist from the start of the process. It seemed better to go with her expertise just now, than to wait a couple of hours and have to do it by ourselves. She wrote a long letter of explanation. We were referred to the Accident and Emergency at the Southern General. Another journey, waiting in another room full of anxious people. The nurse was lovely, and took us through. All the usual test were done – blood pressure, heart, X-ray. They decided to admit Colin, and although I was uncertain, it was the better of the two options. What could I have done at home?

In the first ward, I went to visit the next day. I thought he might still be a bit confused or show indicators of seizure activity. To my surprise, that was not the major characteristic of this visit. Colin was confused – but more as if he had had a urinary tract infection . He seemed to think he was going to a football match, and kept saying to everyone that he would see them at the match. He thought the man in the bed next to him was his old friend's dad (from 30 years ago). He kept asking him if he knew Steve? At one point Colin said 'I am not James T. Taggart' (a wonderful mix up between James T Kirk and Taggart). Colin knew who I was, but was very slow to answer questions, and sometimes lost concentration all together. His eyes kept moving all round the room, as if he could see something move that no-one else could. Maybe angels. I said to the nurse that his behaviours were outwith normal patterns. I also said that he might become agitated, and that he could be given something tablet wise if this occurred. The nurse said he would pass this on to the night shift.

The next day, I read Colin's notes at the end of his bed. Being round hospitals a bit more, you develop these bad habits. It said at 00.30 Colin was given intravenous diazepam. I could tell there had been 'an incident'. I asked the nurse, but she didn't seem to know anything about it – just that he had been a bit sleepy that morning. Colin was still confused: he said he hadn't had his medication, had not been given any food or a cup of tea or coffee. It was Friday afternoon, and there were no test results back. This time they had carried out an EEG etc, which was good, but it was coming up to the weekend, and I asked if I could speak to someone. I was asked to stay a while longer, as a doctor would come. Later on he appeared, bringing good news – the EEG was fine, the blood tests were ok, and there was no inflammation of the brain or anything like this. Colin said he had been passed from place to place, and the doctor gave a three minute description of the ward system in the hospital , and why wards got changed. Colin said the same again. I asked to speak to the doctor, and he said that there seemed to be no reason as to why Colin was reacting like this, it could be a reaction to the slight infection, but that the neurologist had discussed it, and not come up with anything.

The next day, I took Andrew in. Colin was much better. A neurologist was just leaving, and I spoke to him and he said the same all over again. He said that the confusing thing was that e.g. Colin was so slow in his speech, but his reactions were fast – he caught something that fell of the bed. He explained that confusion usually covered all parts of the brain, and not just some, and that was why it didn't add up. He said there was nothing organic that they could see causing this from the tests, and he should go back to see the psychiatrist.

The next day I visited, Colin was much better. He had showered and shaved; his wound on his back was better. He was worried that he couldn't find a mirror, but apart from that he seemed fine, and wanting to go home. From his chart, I saw he had been put on phosphorous tablets, and I asked the nurses at the nurses' station what that was for. One said phosphorous was for bones, and wasn't it quite unstable because it was used in science experiments at school to burn off gas. Another said that phosphorous was round about volcanos. These were not very helpful answers. They did look it up in a medical book on the ward, and she said that not all the pages were in it, as the doctors took the good medical reference books, and left the nurses with the rest. I looked it up myself when I got home - for bones, pain relief, and relief of inflammation. Interesting! As usual – what is its significance? That I was left to puzzle out myself.

On the phone, we were told that Colin could get out on the Monday, late afternoon. I collected Andrew from school, and we arrived at 4pm. Colin looked woosy, slow and unfocussed and was in his hospital gown. I knew just by looking at him that he had had a seizure. I spoke to the nurse; she looked a bit vague, and said she thought so. I looked up his notes at the end of the bed, and it said that he had had two seizures. I started to try and get him changed, but he was very unresponsive. I spoke to the nurse at the desk, and she said his medication still had to be sent up from the pharmacy, and that it could be a while yet. She said we should go away for a while and come back. It could be that I was tired, but the way she said it seemed to imply that I should have known better than to come so early. I was tempted to stay as I thought it would probably take an hour to get him dressed, but I thought it would be better to take Andrew out the way and go to the coffee shop. On the way back, I said to Andrew, 'Let's say a prayer that the nurse is a bit less sharp that she was earlier on.'

When we arrived back in the ward, the good news was that Colin was dressed to go home. The bad news was that there was still no sign of his medication. The nurse started asking Andrew what age he was, and did he like school. She said it was a shame that we had had to wait so long. She said it was very hot, and that she could get us both an ice cream. We said yes, and wondered that this prayer seemed to have been so well answered.! Another 45 minutes of sitting in the corridor, and the medication came, and we were away! Getting Colin to the car was a bit of a challenge as he was very slow, but I think he knew he was going home, and that motivated his journey a bit more.

When we got Colin home, we made an appointment with the nurse at the GP's practice to look at his wound. She took one look at it, and said it was still infected. The wound had sterri strips on it, but was not packed. It looked as if that was what had happened in his stay in the hospital – that the nurses had not really paid attention to the wound on his back. The nurse at the practice redressed it regularly, the doctor came in, and more anti-biotics were prescribed. It still looked bad, and a week later they were talking of Colin having to go back to see the surgeon to get the wound re-opened. Fortunately, eventually, the anti-biotics plus the excellent nursing care from the Practice started to bring results, the wound was less sore and inflamed, and started to look healthier.

It took five weeks after the surgical procedure for Colin's wound to look healthier. By this time we were meant to be going back to Florida on holiday. I had to get additional insurance, and got one of the higher risk companies to cover it. The GP gave us a letter to say we were fit to fly. By this time, I was in two minds. Was it too much to think that Colin could fly? One of the nurses asked Colin if he was looking forward to his holiday, and he said not really. Was I asking him to do something that was too difficult? After such a long palaver, and two sets of anti-biotics, Colin was very tired. His parents suggested that they would take him if he was ill on the day we were due to fly. This was a relief, as Andrew was really looking forward to going. Two days beforehand, Colin seemed a bit more enthusiastic about travelling. His behaviour was a bit erratic however. He had a seizure two days before, but was ok on the morning.

As we started to leave, I couldn't help but notice all the things that Colin couldn't do for himself. I had to pack his bag, although he added some extra things at the last minute. At security the girl spent ages looking at his bag, where Colin had packed his aerosol – instantly put in the bin by the security girl. Then she found his manicure set which he had added, containing two pairs of scissors, also binned. Then he was not allowed to go though the gate because of his vagus nerve stimulator, so had to be searched by hand. After all this we went though a perfume/aftershave aisle where the girl offered Colin a tester to smell some aftershave, but he completely missed what she was talking about and wondered why she was handing what looked like a used match stick. In the airport passenger waiting area, Colin was grumpy at all the announcements that were too loud on the tannoy. As we settled on the plane, opposite two babies (11 months old), Colin complained loudly at the noise they made. I said to him they were just babies, but he hissed back fiercely that they shouldn't be so loud. It was going to be some flight!

In actuality Colin endured the flight reasonably well. It was when we arrived that his tiredness started to show as irritability. In a small hotel room this was not good. His fights with the toilet seat became legendary, and his frustration obvious. No-one else could get into the bathroom, so Andrew and I had to go down to the lobby! In the middle of the night, Colin could not get the toilet to flush properly, so he kept flushing it – as a result it overflowed big time, all over the floor, bedroom carpet etc.

On the second day it rained, and I got a bad cold. Colin didn't like me sneezing, so this was a bit of a problem. There wasn't much space for us in the car, given how my sneezing was annoying Colin! And of course it was raining and a stressful drive. Boy was I glad we could get to our friend's house the next day, so I could go to bed, and they could look after Colin and Andrew. What a blessing.

In retrospect, Colin probably wasn't well enough to go on holiday. He didn't have lots of seizures, but he was very sleepy and irritable.

When we got back home, Colin had a procedure to remove a cyst from his eyelid. He was put on antibiotics for 8 weeks. He seemed to be a little better. We went back to see the neuro-psychiatrist, who was very helpful. He suggested that Colin could have midazolam after each seizure to prevent unusual behaviour and second seizures. For a few months it seemed to work a bit. Colin seemed a little brighter, and didn't have any double seizures. Then it all crashed again, and we were back to six seizures a month, and a double amongst them by October. And when Colin is down at this rate these days, he is very poorly indeed. He couldn't go to his mum and dad's flat one Tuesday after a double seizure. He slept till 4pm, and then wandered round the house, not seeming to recognise where he was. He didn't try to go out the door, so at least that was helpful.

At our next meeting with the neuro-psychiatrist, he had read Colin's notes. This sounds like an encouraging fact, but the outcome was mixed. This time he talked about Colin's psychotic episodes as unexplained, and commented that they could be psychological in nature. I protested, and felt that I was written off. He tried to give me strategies for calming someone down if they are agitated. Needless to say the notes from Colin's last hospital admission weren't there – which would have showed that when Colin became agitated in the ward, they gave him intravenous diazepam at 2am! Yet I'm to use calming words. What on earth does he think I do every day anyway, and such strategies seem to bear very little fruit.

Our visit to the GP went in a similar fashion. Sporadically over the last 6 months Colin's eyes have become red and swollen – the lids, as well as the eyes themselves being red and sore. It usually lasts about 10 minutes, and then they recover. The doctor said he had never heard of this before. Then he said it could be a blocked tear duct, but that it was unlikely that both tear ducts would block at the same time. Really helpful! You feel sometimes as if the doctor thinks you are making it all up, just to keep him busy. And it is anything but.

At the Remembrance service this year, it was so poignant. Listening to these amazing words about remembering and finding meaning. Colin was there. He wore a suit, the first time since last Remembrance day. He had a seizure this morning, and it took him an hour to get ready, and to come down to the service – to get a shirt and tie on, and his military cap. This is true courage! Yet so sad. He wanted to commemorate his fallen comrades, and to be acknowledged himself. It is the only day each year that this happens. How can we say such amazing words about honouring those who serve, and yet let people down so badly once they are retired and back home, maimed and in pain. It is obscene. I feel so angry that no-one seems to be in place to acknowledge his situation, his hurt, his frustration. He is not always believed, because he is different, and somehow therefore less credible. And yet his pain is just as real.

Some Answers

The GP helpfully referred Colin to see an opthalmologist regarding his eyes. We went along, and waited in the waiting room. A man came out and took Colin in to check out his eyes. He did various tests, and said that Colin's eyesight was very poor, and where were his glasses? I had to say I didn't know, as Colin didn't really wear them. The man looked at us in astonishment, and said that Colin should wear them. It was a very straightforward matter to him! I tried to explain that we understood that, but that it wasn't really our first priority in life. The man said that he didn't want to judge us, but that really Colin should wear his glasses as he is very short-sighted. He was a bit impatient in giving Colin instructions as to how to use the machine, and did not seem very 'in tune'.

However, despite the lack of empathy to Colin (our nine year old son said, 'That man wasn't very nice to daddy'), he also gave us some answers. He said that Colin had a form of bletharitis,*29 which affected his eyes. He then sold us some eyelid wipes and some eye drops, with instructions as to how to use them, and saying that Colin would need to use these for the rest of his life. I resisted the temptation to try to tell the man that following his detailed instructions for every day treatment of Colin's eye conditions was an impossibility for us to follow. Colin's life style was too chaotic, and he was too impatient and short tempered to follow such instructions. Yet using the eye drops now and again could at least reduce irritability for his eyes, which would be something.

The other benefit from this interview, which I pondered over for a long time, was that the strange description of what happened to Colin's eyes had some medical basis in fact. The opthalmologist had listened to our description of symptoms, and made sense of them. He said that the eyes would become watery, sore and swollen when Colin was concentrating on something, and that these symptoms would be intermittent. Therefore the symptoms that we described were accurate and authentic, even though the GP had been a bit dismissive of us. It renewed my strength to remember that GPs do not have all the answers, and that sometimes the patient can actually be correct. In many ways this was very affirming.

In December 2010, we had an appointment with the neuro-psychiatrist. I had felt that he was very good in the past, although I had some questions about the summary letter from our last visit. Colin wasn't very well that day, but he managed to come along with me. It was hard to wake him up, and get him out the door for 11.30am, to get to our 12 noon appointment. I had to wake him up, give him his tablets with some tea, and encourage him to go to the toilet, before putting his jacket and shoes on and getting him to the car.

By the time we got there, I was trying to work out what questions to ask. We went in, and the doctor asked Colin a few questions – did he remember seeing him (Colin nodded), why had he come (to see if he could help his epilepsy) etc. In some of his answers, Colin seemed to have only a very fuzzy grasp of the question, and was very slow. He started speaking about his time in the military, and lost the thread of the conversation entirely. The doctor seemed to realise how ill Colin was.

He told us he had managed to find the notes from Colin's May hospital admission, and that having studied them, he had had some thoughts. Colin's confused state seemed not to be from his epilepsy or post-ictal condition or disordered brain function, but from a delirium from his low grade infection. His theory was that Colin's brain was like that of an old man and was very susceptible to confusion – even from quite a mild infection.

For the first time, we seemed to have an answer for what had been happening for the last three years: a relief, but obviously not good news about Colin's condition. If it happened again, then I would still need to go through the same steps of consulting with the GP, hospitalisation etc. The doctor said that the man he saw before him was not the same man he had read of in the notes; he felt that there had been significant background deterioration, and that he wanted to run some tests to look at this. He nodded to me, and I nodded back, and then he said to Colin – do you realise that your condition is deteriorating? Colin said he thought he was getting better. The doctor said that he wanted Colin to be aware that his situation wasn't getting any better. Colin just looked at him. The doctor said he would make three appointments for the next year for us, and that we needed to keep phoning the social work department to get more support for us in the house.

Regarding the use of anti-psychotic drugs – he gave us a very reasoned and balanced series of options to think about. The down side is that they could lower Colin's seizure threshold, which would be negative. Yet a small dose could be introduced gradually, to see if they helped. The positive side is that they could stabilise Colin's mood a bit, which would could e.g. lessen his irritability. We would need to think about this. In the end, it seemed the best solution, and we could go forward with a low dose of an antipsychotic.

It was really an excellent appointment in that the doctor was helpful, knowledgeable, had read all the notes (some feat in itself), and was very focussed. His explanation was so helpful, but the underlying meaning was pretty negative. In the coffee room afterwards, we went for some lunch, and I followed up on the conversation, saying to Colin did he realise that perhaps there would come a day in the future when we wouldn't be able to look after him in the house any more. He said ok – how much would it cost, and could Gerard (his carer) still come to visit him? I knew he hadn't

COLIN – PROUDER AND HAPPIER DAYS

really taken it in, but it was a start for the next part of the process.

2010

I have decided to stop writing about Colin for a while – it is just too awful for words. His seizures are relentless, and his deterioration continues apace. I keep thinking maybe it is just a bad few months, but the reality is that things are just getting worse and worse. For the most part he is not aware – just functioning – and that is better than the anguish of him realising what is happening to him.

If you ever see a dishevelled man at the roadside, staggering about and shouting – do not dismiss him. He could be Colin, or any one of our veterans or brain injured people, confused and unhappy. As a society, we need to reflect as to whether there is any more we can do. As individuals, we need to show them compassion and love.

'There is a comfort in the strength of love;
'Twill make a thing endurable, which else
Would overset the brain, or break the heart.'

William Wordsworth

Chapter 13

A NEW HOME FOR COLIN

'What if your blessing comes through rain drops,
What if your healing comes through tears.
What if a thousand sleepless nights are what it takes to know You are near,
What if the trials in your life are Your mercies in disguise.'

Song 'Blessings', by Laura Story (also in her eponymous book by Worthy Publishing, © Hachette, Nashville 2012)

'In quietness and trust is your strength'

Isaiah 30:15

The Events of 2013-14

After many years of feeling that we were about to fall off a cliff, it finally happened. After a relentless stream of more difficult days, and increased number of carers, Colin was not doing so well. The deterioration was ongoing. In the autumn of 2012, Colin was noticeably less well. He sometimes slept from midnight till 4pm in the afternoon for no apparent reason. He would sometimes seem to have seizure activity between seizures – periods when he would be unintentionally drumming his fingers, or when they would be splayed outright and motionless. Sometimes he would be sitting looking absent-mindedly into space. His motivation to do things was much reduced, and he could be very frustrated and aggressive, sensitive to the least noise, shouting at shadows.

One of the memories that haunted Colin, was about when he first started on active duty . . .

Coming to Belfast – a first experience of military life

After graduating from the School of Military Intelligence (Ashford), I was given my first official posting with an English Regiment in Belfast (N.I.) which was presumably to 'break me in'. I had no previous experience (street patrolling / riot control / cooking for the whole regiment / terrorist attacks and bombs and booby traps) and had no idea of what I was walking into.

First day, on my arrival at the Barracks in Belfast, I was regarded as something of a peculiarity. 'What the fuck are you doing with us?' and received numerous questioning stares: 'What is a member of the Intelligence Corp doing by himself with us?' By day two, I was on my first street patrol and receiving even more questioning stares. I thought I was getting the 'hang' of this, and felt quite confident in myself.

Then the soldier I got to know as 'Jake' tripped the booby trap in the bin he was searching and blew himself apart. The shock wave blew me and anybody else within 100 yards right off our feet. The first thing I remember was thinking, 'Why am I lying on the road, holding my rifle studying the gutter in front of my nose?'. Then I remembered 'Jake' and started pulling myself together.

That wasn't so difficult, and with a few initial wobbly steps I walked almost normally across the road to the bin to see if I could help. I was met by the Sergeant who gave me a brush and walked past me with the words 'I'll get a tarpaulin sheet'. I looked at 'Jake' and saw he was already dead. Head practically blown off and body ripped wide open, there was a lot of 'Jake' lying about. I wasn't so keen about helping now. More members of the Regiment appeared and grew in numbers.

The Sergeant was back quickly with the tarpaulin sheet and told me abruptly, 'Start sweeping him up'. I dumped my kit and rifle with another member of the unit/company and started on 'Jake', I wasn't sure if the soldiers who had turned up were there to help or just for a stare at the horror show. I got on with my job and tried not to think about him, but I did, too much.

I kept thinking about him being the same age as me, how we had been chatting like assured friends just an hour before, when the Sergeant gave us a 'bollocking' for chatting like teenagers and not concentrating on our jobs enough. 'What the fuck do you think the Army pays you for? So you can indulge in chit-chat with your pals? I expect you two to be a part of this unit, with your thoughts and eyes constantly about you, and watching the back of the next guy up the street, and the rest of the street. There's no place for wankers like you two. If you don't want to be a part of this Regiment, then fuck off! I'll arrange the discharge papers for you.' We apologised to him (he was quite right, we were both in error) and started trying to be 'professional' soldiers.

I finished with 'Jake', and four other soldiers picked up the sheet and put it into the Ambulance that had arrived. The Sergeant told me to 'put the brush with the body' and I did so. Then the soldier who'd been keeping my kit gave it back to me with the comment he didn't envy my job. I told him I didn't either and started moving further up the street with the rest of the unit. I could already tell I was going to find the incident difficult with my thoughts that evening.

Later on with a pat on the shoulder, the Sergeant told me, 'I'll speak to you later', and walked on to the front of the line. I thought I was going to get an even bigger 'bollocking' for my earlier failing. But he hadn't specified so I was just guessing and the only thing I knew I'd done wrong was the chat with 'Jake' earlier, so what else could it be?

Throughout the rest of the day my mind became more focused concentrating on the job of patrolling along a street, which helped strengthen my resolve, although I felt sincerely unhappy about the whole incident. I even felt quite self confident with my ability to 'soldier' as required. Come the end of the day I was feeling very tired and washed out, glad to see the Barracks as we turned the corner. I'd also noticed just how intensively nervous the other members of the unit were about 'checking' anything, and rightly assumed they were no more experienced on this that I was. The only one who knew anything was the Sergeant and he grew to be a kind of 'father' figure, intensely hated by a lot of the soldiers for a lot of reasons, but very reliable.

Glad to take my Bergen off my back and stretch out on my bed, I went to sleep almost immediately. I woke up to the Sergeant looking down on me, which completely startled me. 'Come on Gardner, off your arse, you've slept long enough, the Major wants a word with you, get moving'. So I rolled out of bed already fully dressed, the Sergeant finished my preparations with the words, 'That's all you'll need,' and threw my beret at me. 'Now comb your hair.' Other members of the unit were already sitting up, taking an interest in the Sergeant's visit.

As we walked out of the barracks I caught a few questioning stares. Shrugging my shoulders, I walked out after the Sergeant, who caught my arm as I came out the door, as if he wasn't going to risk letting me walk off again. I queried the Sergeant as to why the Major was there, wanting to talk to me. He wasn't communicative and just smiled and stated, 'You'll be alright, and you're not here for anything you shouldn't be'. I still didn't know much about anything by the time we reached the Major's office. The Sergeant abruptly told me, 'Knock on the door and announce our presence'. Which I did so calling out, 'Sergeant and Private Gardner here at Major's request.' The Sergeant slapped me on the shoulder and added that it was 'smart' and correct procedure to use. I took the compliment but I was only guessing as to what to say and could just as easily have made a mess of the whole statement.

As the Major's voice resounded out, inviting us to enter, I took the door handle nervously, opened the door and invited the Sergeant to be first to enter. He did so and I anticipated he had been planning this all day. I didn't feel any more confident than I had felt earlier on. By the time I was in the Major's office the Sergeant was sitting beside him behind the Major's desk. Both staring at me as it I was standing trial for some grievous offence, which was just how I felt. I saw my standing territory shrivel up before the Major's desk.

'At ease Gardner, you're not here on trial' was what the Major first addressed me with. 'You're actually here to be complimented for your actions today concerning Private Jordan, a most unfortunate incident. I appreciate the two of you were forming a friendship and your work cleaning him up was no small task; however that is what they pay us for. The fact that you completed the task and carried on with the street patrol, which the Sergeant has informed me you performed excellently, fulfilling your duties as a soldier and a credit to this Regiment'.

These memories, and the deep grieving and traumatic emotions evoked, were often not far from the surface of Colin's life, even thirty years later. His startle reactions were strong, exacerbated by his debilitating brain injury, which meant his outburst of rage were powerful and long lasting.

Colin would get angry if the phone rang, so we unplugged it downstairs. He would be furious if the doorbell rang, and so we took the battery out. Colin arriving at the door to greet the window cleaner was a risk too many, so we stopped getting the windows cleaned. We just couldn't predict his behaviour. We would tip toe through the room Colin fell asleep in, to avoid waking him, or sometimes it was easier to go outside to get to the kitchen, rather than to disturb him, even in the rain. For Andrew especially, this made his life so very difficult, as it was impossible to have his friends in.

We would take Colin out to the University café or the local garden centre, but it could be hard going. Balancing the food on a tray, and trying to support Colin so he didn't fall over, was a bit of an art form. Every now and again, someone behind the counter would offer a hand, and I was so grateful for their thoughtfulness. Occasionally Colin would fall asleep at the table after eating, and it wasn't worth trying to wake him up. We could be there for a while, as I didn't want him to growl and make a scene. Sitting at a table in a café, praying for Colin to wake up and be in a good mood, so we could leave peaceably, was not fun.

In October 2012, Colin's dad had an art exhibition at the willow tea room, and we all went along to the private viewing. Colin did well, and enjoyed chatting to everyone, even though he did not always know who they were. He was in his element that night. However the next day, he was not so well. Colin had a group of seizures, from which he didn't quite seem to recover. He was very sleepy, very unresponsive, not even eating or drinking a great deal. He seemed to have forgotten how to use his fork, to move it up and down from the plate, in order to get food and drink into his mouth.

After a poor week, I called the emergency doctor out to see him on the Friday evening. We managed to get a urine sample, and it seemed clear. The GP said I should help him to drink with a straw, and use a fork to help him to eat, because if he was reminded what to do, there would be a following on momentum to continue, for he was hungry. And once I started to feed him with a fork, he coped a lot better, at least eating a little. The doctor said he could be admitted to hospital, but they wouldn't necessarily treat him, so I just kept him at home. He lowered his dose of beta blockers, in case that was responsible for slowing Colin down.

In November, we had another week which was similar. Colin was again sluggish and unresponsive, having seizure activity, and poorly. I could give him 2mg diazepam, but it made no difference. It might make him sleepy, but it did not stop the seizure activity. For this kind of episode to have happened twice in four weeks, made me wonder if there was some kind of infection underneath, and so I phoned the doctor's surgery. It was a Tuesday – 20th November. After some phone calls back and forward during the course of the day, they decided he should be admitted to hospital, for them to check him out. I asked for Colin to go to the hospital with a neurological department where Colin was known.

Even though the hospital knew Colin was coming and why, we still had to go through accident and emergency. They gave Colin an EEG and a chest x-ray. One of the nurses remembered Colin from being in before. They took blood tests. I asked if they wanted to know Colin's medication, but they said this was unnecessary, as they had all the information from the GP's practice. Yet when I looked at it, the computerised information was out of date. They would have given Colin the old dosage of beta blocker. Eventually after 5 hours, he was admitted into a receiving ward. It was after 11pm, and as there were no doctors around I went home. In A and E, I explained about Colin being a bit jerky, and that this was seizure activity, and the staff just look at you and say nothing. They look at you, as if you are making things up, just for the fun of it. You feel like you are talking a different language.

Over the next two days in the receiving ward, it was standard practice we were well used to. They take blood tests which will take a few days to get back. They order a scan, which takes a while to be scheduled. And meanwhile there is no treatment, in case that masks what might be going on. Colin still twitching from time to time, and slow. On the Friday, he was transferred to an acute medical ward – ward 23.

On the Saturday, I could see Colin become more agitated. It often seems that after a period of seizure activity, he becomes farther away. He becomes hostile to direction, and confused in himself. It looked like the brink of a psychotic episode, yet no one seemed to be listening. That night, Colin became very agitated, and he was given haloperidol to calm him down. By the next day – the Sunday, he was very distressed, seeing eyes in the woodwork. He said things like 'The world has rejected me, so I will reject the world.' He said, 'I am getting angry and will kill people.' One day, Colin tried to escape out to the car park, and one of the nurses Donna went after him. She said to him that it was raining and she was getting wet, and would he please come back in, and he did so. Even at his least well, he was thinking of others welfare, and as a nurse, she knew the right approach – calm and practical. I give thanks every time a nurse is as sensible as this.

On Sunday, Colin again seemed disturbed and agitated. In the evening at 8.30pm I was at church, when I got a text from Andrew. Colin had gone missing from the ward, and the police had come to the house. I collected Andrew and went up to the hospital, and the police were finishing searching the building, and were looking for him in the grounds. They said that Colin had fallen out with the nursing staff and was agitated, and had been hiding from them. Colin was categorised as a vulnerable patient, and they were making every effort to find him. This was evident from the 20 or so policemen in the lobby, and the helicopters overhead.

It was a freezing cold foggy winter night, and you couldn't see very far in any direction. They told me that Colin didn't have his shoes on, as they were left beside his bed. That detail haunted me, that he could be out on such a bitterly night, and he was out in his bare feet or just his socks. We looked in some of the corridors, and in some of the places Colin was familiar with – the neurology building and café, and the corridors that linked them. There were so many poorly lit corridors and doors and unlit rooms, and after a while I took Andrew home, and after some phone calls, a friend and I went out to look for Colin in the car. We wondered if he might have tried to get home, but the Clyde tunnel is shut to pedestrian traffic at night, and there were no reports of him on CCTV. Then I wondered if he might have tried to go to our old house in Shawlands, and we tried the different roads through Govan and Ibrox. The police searched our house, in case he had made it home and had fallen asleep somewhere. They visited his mum and dad's house, to see if he might have gone there. It was an endless, unrelentlingly bleak night, and my imagination was working overtime. Was he in some outhouse, freezing to death? We went to the Victoria A and E to see if he might have been picked up and gone there. Nothing. Everyone was sympathetic, but no-one had any information. We got a coffee at a KFC, and they gave us it for free, when they heard what we were out doing in the middle of the night.

By 3.30am, we met up with a Sergeant in the mist in the hospital grounds, and he took us back to the police station, to go over all the information again. He thought Colin was still in the hospital somewhere, but I thought it was more likely he would have tried to make it home. The sergeant said if he was outside, and not in shelter, he could be at risk from hypothermia, and that he might not make it. He told me to go home and get a few hours sleep. He suggested sending Andrew to school, but letting the school know his dad was missing. In the morning, hopefully visibility would be better, and there would be more news. They said it they would start to prepare a press release, which would go out to the public, if he still had not been found by morning.

I got a few hours disturbed sleep, and was up at 7am. I emailed the school to let them know what had happened, and had a cup of tea. I took the dog out for a walk at 8am, and when I got back, there was a message, saying Colin had been found on the ward. I phoned back, and they said he had been found in a cupboard. It was Angela – one of the staff nurses that found him. I was relieved, but wondered what state Colin would be in, after missing his tablets, and being in a cupboard overnight. I might have known: he was sitting in his chair, eating toast and drinking tea – still thinking there were strange eyes in the furniture, and still disorientated, but ok. The consultant came to see him, and felt the haloperidol might have had a bad effect, on top of the agitated state he was already in.

Over the next 24 hours, Colin still did not settle, and it was decided the only way to calm him down, was to give him a massive dose of diazepam. Everything changed, and Colin's chances of getting home began to dwindle. In the lucid moments Colin had, he was delighted to know that 25 policemen, with dogs and helicopters were out looking for him. He felt he had been successful in eluding them, and he was proud of that fact. Every time he told the story, the number of police and dogs involved in the search went up. For him, it was a matter of pride – he still had the old undercover skills to elude people. We were too glad to have him in one piece, to mention the expense, time and effort all given up for him.

I always thought hospital wards were places you passed through on the way to somewhere else, but sometimes people get stuck there, and everything changes.

Six months later, I'm sitting here in the bathroom of ward 23 of the local hospital, watching my husband asleep in the bath. There is not a lot happening. All is quiet. The staff have been lovely in letting him stay in the bath as Colin finds it relaxing. Two of the staff, Ian and Lynn have been in to see if we are ok. Lynn has made me a cup of tea. I am crying – every time someone is kind it is overwhelming.

Colin was in this hospital for nine and a half months in total. During that time, his health varied enormously. The diazepam seemed to lift his brain and make it function in a way it had not done for years – he played chess, and talked away. Yet there was a downside too – he felt better and wanted to go back to work, having no insight into his condition. And there was an ambiguity about him too – which I later found out is called lability. When I said to Colin that the seriousness of his condition meant he might not be able to go home, he didn't demur. Naively I thought this meant he had come to terms with it all, but actually it was the drug talking. Colin was not bothered about much, one way or another. We even took him home to collect some things, and he went back to the hospital without question.

When his condition was stable, after a number of weeks, and the drug level started to come down a little, Colin felt hurt and rejected that he could not go home. And yet he was not able too – he was too vulnerable to leave without someone watching him, making sure he was ok, that he was not being aggressive, or having seizures or wandering away. Colin was put on a different drug in the same family – clonazepam, to keep him calmer and to prevent more episodes. As the staff got to know him, and his ways and his mood swings, Colin got used to the ward. He felt he was a self-appointed vigilante, stopping other patients trying to leave without permission, and assisting the nurses in their tasks!

Christmas was hard, but Colin was well enough for us to take him to his brother's house for a family meal, which was great. It was poignant taking him back, and we were locked out because it was after 11pm. We found an open door however, and managed to get Colin back to the ward.

When the decision was made that Colin now needed full time nursing care, the battle was on to try and find the right place. I started looking for nursing homes that would take a younger man with epilepsy and brain damage. I went through the internet seeing what was available in the local councils, and reading the Care Commission reports. Then I visited the ones which seemed to offer the best care – nursing care, a secure location, a bright environment for under 65's. I visited a dozen or more different homes. Some never got back to me after I visited. Some seemed unsure how to deal with Colin's condition, and worried about his behaviour. Some refused to take him outright. Erskine repeatedly refused to take Colin, as it was felt that they could not meet his needs. It was to be a long and eye-opening process. Many places with the best Care Commission reports, only seemed to have these reports because they cherry pick the most docile of patients, and they would refuse to consider Colin as he was too unpredictable for them.

Colin had a rough ride in hospital. Ward 23 doctors and staff did a great job with him, some of them were particularly kind and thoughtful with a great sense of humour, and it made such a difference.

Nurses like Angela, Lynn and Cindy looked out for Colin, and made sure that he was well cared for. Angela was especially kind and went the extra mile, and wrote a wise and insightful report about Colin to be considered by various homes. Nursing auxiliaries such as Karen and Sam got to know Colin well also. I spoke with Karen recently about what it was like to look after Colin. Karen had a special rapport with Colin, through humour and stubbornness and banter.

She spoke about how Colin could have a very loud ferocious roar, which could startle the whole ward, but that inside he was gentle. The challenge with Colin was often to wake him up, get him to take his tablets, and to get him into the shower. He needed to do this, for example taking his tablets at nearly the right time helped prevent seizures. For some staff, it was an impossible thing to get Colin to conform. Karen, and others were good at cajoling Colin. When Colin said 'no', Karen would say, 'Well you can do it the hard way, or the easy way' and Colin would usually comply. Yet Karen gave Colin space when he needed it – you could tell by his face, when he needed space. He might protest that there was no way he wanted washed, but once in the shower, Colin actually loved it, for he found the sensation of the warm water very relaxing. Colin loved to give chess lessons to all who would listen, and be willing to learn, but he did give up trying to teach some individuals, who he felt were beyond learning!

Colin would berate other patients if they gave the nurses a hard time. Once I came in, and couldn't find his alarm clock, and discovered it on the floor at the other side of the ward, and he had thrown it at an annoying patient. Another time, Colin was listening to his music on his headphones, and another patient also had his music on. The doctor on duty thought it was Colin's music that was making the noise, and turned Colin's music off. Colin was incandescent with rage, and called him a 'pompous imbecile' for turning off the wrong patient's music. He did get an apology in the end. Colin did not suffer fools gladly, but he often did it with such a dry humour, that it was hard not to forgive him.

However Colin was still in a respiratory ward, and it was not the best place for him. The discharge nurses kept in constant touch, as did the social worker, trying to find a suitable place. In their enthusiasm, they recommended places that were far away, which had been closed due to poor care practices etc. Colin got some infections in the ward, and at the end of July aspirated one night. I didn't know this word, till the nurse phoned to tell me. He was so ill, and ironically it was probably because he was in the right ward, that he got effective treatment quickly which saved his life. There was another night spent, watching Colin's blood pressure going down to 65/30, his stats looking horrendous, but he fought back in typical fashion, and lived to fight another day.

The week before Colin was to leave the ward was hard. He had got used to life in ward 23. I took him to see the home, where he was likely to go, and everyone went out of their way to be kind, and to make him at home, but it was a shock to his system, and to mine. Although I had worked towards this for so long, seeing him there was emotionally draining – I felt guilty, that I had not tried hard enough, that I was responsible. We often say that *we* put someone into care, but I think this is misleading: it was *Colin's disability* that took him into care, and the continued underlying deterioration in his condition, and that was so difficult to come to terms with. He needed 24 hour care, and this was something I could not give. Despite the rational part of me knowing this, the guilt never left me.

On the day he was to be transferred, I came to pick him up, and the ward had his medication and everything ready. Colin had just stopped antibiotics for another UTI, and was slow and not very responsive. I packed up his belongings, of which there were many. Tears streamed down my face, as this ward had been our home for all this time – it was familiar, and the staff were kind and helpful. Saying goodbye to everyone was excruciating. For 9 months, this had been Colin's home – a bed and a bedside locker – and a team of people that had become like family. This had become our world.

Bringing Colin to the home Craigielea Care Home was hard too. Physically, we had made all the preparations – got all the furniture for his room, his paintings and books and bits and pieces. We got out of the car, and I sat and had a cup of tea with Colin in the 'den', and talked about him having his own room and toilet, the pleasant garden outside etc. Colin looked blankly at me. Words just seemed so hollow and irrelevant to the essence of what was happening. And every time I left and went out the door of the Home for the first few weeks I cried my eyes out. There was something so awful about leaving him with people I didn't know very well. Even though the rational part of my brain knew this was what Colin needed, my heart felt broken. The ongoing grieving process is so very tough. Colin being in the home reminded me of the nature of his condition, and that any possibility of a more regular family life was now gone. There were losses on so many levels. It was not just the loss of Colin's health, but also the loss of our dreams as individuals and as a family.

Now we were to start on a new chapter, and it was permanent and final. Colin had now been there for eight weeks, and he was adjusting gradually. The manager Sheila had the goodness to accept Colin as a resident, even though she knew he could be difficult, but she had confidence that her staff were trained and professional, and that they would be able to cope. I am grateful to them, and we are finding our way forward. On good days I can take Colin out for a coffee, and Andrew and I take the dog up to see him. On bad days, he is growly and sleepy, and wants to have his own space. This is our new life.

COLIN AND HIS DOG JACK

Chapter 14

THE LAST LAP

'Compassion is the quivering of the heart in response to another's suffering.'

Mary Jo Meadow

'After the last tear falls, there is love.'

Andrew Peterson

'I'll keep coming home'

Runrig

Colin was in the nursing home for four and a half years. At the beginning, it was tough, I felt guilty, Colin was unsettled and angry. The staff didn't always understand Colin, but they treated him with dignity and respect. Colin loved regaling the night staff with his military stories at 1am in the morning. This was one of them.

Guatemala 1978

Looking through the window beside me, I could see the line of the river, the helicopter was following and already knew each twist and turn the river would take. No lights were on inside the helicopter for security sake, but with 12 men, 12 fully laden Bergens and a considerable amount of equipment for the six week period, things were getting pretty crowded least of all in my own mind. Was I really up to the standard required? Yes, I had received four and a half years of anti terrorist experience in Northern Ireland at a time when terrorist activity was at its most intense.

I had worked for three and a half years with S.M.I.U. (Special Military Intelligence Unit) establishing and starting the first R.C.S. (Regional Crime Squad) in Northern Ireland; I took a certain pride in my involvement. There had been several involvements with the S.A.S., which had obviously pleased Col. Peter de la Billiére or Col. De Beers as he was nicknamed by the Unit and had probably swung it in my favour to be part of the operation. The nickname came about because of the western culture and the English speaking population not having the ability to pronounce the Colonel's name correctly. In Northern Ireland my first posting was six months with the English Regiment to 'break me in' which it certainly did, although I never anticipated ending up as their 'Chief'.

Sent from Northern Ireland to Wales on 'fitness training', which was S.A.S training for four months. On completion of which I was sent to Belize, I still did not have any idea as to what 'fitness training' really meant, beyond it being noticed that I had been drinking too much whilst with the R.C.S. (two years R.U.C.) and was consequently seriously below fitness standards.

On arrival in Belize I had my interview with Col. de Beers, later promoted to General in Command First Gulf war. He explained about the intended Guatemalan operation, three units of 12, and three units of four in each unit, at the invitation of Guatemalan Government, to assist with a problem of civil war they couldn't handle. To be flown in by helicopter at night in two weeks time, operation would take six weeks. Their civil war was deteriorating down into something like 'gang' warfare. Two weeks would be all the preparation allowed for the operation. Colonel said work in Northern Ireland made it okay to go on operation as Military Intelligence although I would be expected to perform as any other unit member, but any indication of 'fallen behind' and I would be 'removed' in no uncertain terms, from the operation.

Before being flown out to Belize, and my first briefing about the operation, I certainly knew the standards of the S.A.S. and whilst I felt assured to be surrounded by members of the finest regiment in the world, I also felt very aware of my own isolation. I knew if I wasn't up to their standards, I'd be out in an instant, no second chances, no excuses, very much on my own.

The three units of 12 climbed into the three helicopters shortly after midnight and took off from Belize runway heading for Guatemala. The moon was at its lowest and the sky was overcast with clouds everywhere, conditions were perfect. We had already received warnings in the last two weeks that any units of the Guatemalan forces were sufficiently well equipped to take us out of the air, if seen. The emphasis was to keep a very low profile and don't be spotted (not even going to the toilet). Stay three to four days ahead of our booby traps.

Within 30 minutes, we had crossed the border into Guatemala and were following the line of the river down the valley to the base of the mountains. The helicopters were moving really fast and flying low. I did not know a helicopter could move so fast. I was about to be educated in quite a lot of things in that operation. We had been studying maps for the last two weeks so we knew the area by heart. Our mission was to find which one of the factions was wrecking the Indian villages and use booby traps to scare them off. We had already split up into our three different mission areas before crossing the border and knew as soon as we crossed the border we were literally on our own and would be for the next six weeks.

The helicopter landed at the base of the mountains and the standard four man box pattern was established around us for protection, while the rest of us unloaded men and equipment as fast as possible. When the helicopter was ready to leave the pilot started up the engine and opened his side window, leaning out to call a last message to the C.O. (Commanding Officer), 'I will be back for you at this exact spot in six weeks time, don't be late,' and promptly took off. Some men gave the raised 3rd finger sign for 'Fuck You' and started sorting out the equipment and who would carry what.

I was allocated the radio, spare batteries, video camera, and maps which seemed appropriate for an Intelligence Officer to carry. But the radio combined with all my own gear and a very large mountain to walk up, made me very aware of the weight of my Bergen and the warning from my Colonel about 'falling behind'. When everyone was geared up we set off up the mountain and moved with the rest of the unit to find our first indications of military involvement. The other two units were at different locations.

The jungle felt like it was about to start pouring with rain. You could literally feel the water oozing out of the trees and the other plants. You could almost breathe it in where you stood and wondered what effect this was having on your lungs. When I sneaked side-looks at my colleagues, and managed to catch them off guard, I realised they weren't so elite as their reputation seemed to give them credit for, or so I thought. They were about to educate me in quite a lot of areas over the next six weeks.

After four hours slog we came to the first Indian village that showed signs of indications of military involvement. The reception from the inhabitants wasn't quite what we had expected; we had actually hoped to improve on our information by finding out from the villagers who was responsible for wrecking the Indians' villages, and whereabouts we could find them. Instead, at the first sight of our soldiers the villagers had displayed fear and ran off to hide. The one man in our unit trained to use the Indian language had called out, 'Wait please, we are British, we know about the soldiers attacking your villages and we are here to help you. Our soldiers you can see standing outside your village will not advance any further without your explicit consent'. I don't know what the Indians thought about the British, but he managed to persuade the two who waited to stay for a talk, share opinions and information about their problem.

We would explain why we were here and what we intended to do and how we would achieve this. They agreed and started walking back into the centre of the village. Had we been soldiers planning an undercover attack, we could have shot them now and more of the village when they returned. Our linguist was very capable, very intelligent, and very far sighted. In minutes, he had turned a possible disaster right around, and got the operation started.

It was now nearly 5.00am, the sky was starting to light up, morning sun rise wouldn't be far away. I knew I'd missed the night, until tomorrow anyway but could I have used some sleep right now, I was knackered. I watched the linguist and the Indians as they met in the village centre and started to talk. The longer and more detailed the conversation became, the more confident the Indians were about being in our presence. Within minutes, the C.O. was beside the linguist chatting to the Indians. Then our Sergeant was beside me, 'Boss wants you'. Pointing at the grouping I nodded to show I understood and gave my gun and spare ammo to the Sergeant. Then I moved into the village and when beside the C.O. and the rest of the group, I just crouched down and waited for the C.O. to say something. I listened to the linguist translating for the group but realised how ignorant I was. Then the C.O. was asking me for a map of the area. I nodded to him and started to take my Bergen off.

God, it was good to have my back free of that load, even if it was only for a few minutes. I opened the Bergen at the top whereabouts all the maps were and by pure fate or luck, I found the precise map, at my first search. C.O. must have thought I was 'efficient' or something. I put everything else back into the Bergen and put that back on. Such was my luck the villagers seemed a lot more confident about talking to us and had already used the high degree ordinance survey map of the area I produced to indicate which other villages in the area they thought had already been hit and those due to be hit and why.

They described the military units as being highly efficient, very well equipped with high level technology. The units had been wearing camouflage paint over their faces just like ourselves, which as why the Indians had been initially so afraid of us. They were sure the soldiers were not Guatemalan and even suggested they could possibly be American. This was giving us ideas to work with. We thanked them for their help and told them we would be moving to the next village to see if there were any signs of the soldiers. We praised them for their courage and asked if we could take water from their well before leaving their village. They trusted us sufficiently that they agreed.

What we didn't know was that the Guatemala Government had already sent units to investigate the wrecked villages and in so doing, had informed them of the highly secret information, that British units were to be expected, who would deal with which ever faction was responsible for wrecking the villages. However, the Guatemalan Government could not cope with their civil war and foresaw it breaking down into gang warfare. That was until we arrived.

What we and the Guatemalan Government also didn't know, but ought to have surmised easily enough, was that the US had political and military interest in an area that had just discovered oil and were not going to risk not having a share in the oil revenues.

At the next village we set up a 'surveillance team' and waited for the 'soldiers' to arrive. The Indians had already left the village in anticipation of the coming soldiers and were quite prepared to leave it to us to fight any battles with malignant factions. We had resigned ourselves to sitting in our respective mud holes completely covered with camouflage paint, local bushes, leaves and branches from trees, and waiting for what turned out to be all of four days. The fact that it rained for each of those four days had little to do with it, units of the S.A.S. were not expected to be troubled by such things. But the rain seemed to get continually heavier and heavier. Was I going to drown in my first mud hole, all in the line of duty?

Meanwhile, my thoughts continued to wander, in a mud hole for four days there isn't a hell of a lot to keep your mind focused on. I'd noticed in the first week that other members of the unit were studying me. I had assumed they were assessing my standards of performance, when actually they were rather confused as to why a M.I. Officer with no record of any S.A.S. training or assessment would be with them; some even thought I was there to assess them. However, by the end of the first week, all misunderstandings were cleared up, or so we thought. That was when we tripped over those 'soldiers' instigating their policy of destroying Indian villages as an example to the other factions in the civil war and to de-stabilise the Guatemalan Government.

Which gave way to a resounding shock. We were looking at U.S. Marines, now in line with our guns and cameras. 'What do we do now sir?' So we pooled our resources of four, and agreed that with too many Marines, so few of us, no booby traps set, there was not a lot we could do for this particular village. Except watch them whilst they methodically destroyed the empty village piece by piece, whilst we recorded the entire process on video film. With the wrecking of the various villages and the video film for evidence, it fairly wrapped things up for the Americans.

As the only M.I. Officer in the unit, it was expected by the others that I should contact our bosses, if and when necessary, and avoid the potential for a diplomatic incident. I had anticipated that it was bigger than our bosses and would probably have gone as high as the P.M. and the White House.

We received a quick reply, which was not expected, and came across the radio something like this, 'Gardner, are you responsible for getting this unit involved with Americans?'

My response was, 'Who told you that rubbish?' Which came back as, 'you did'. My answer was to tell him that U.S. Marines had been wrecking Indian villages as an example to other factions in the civil war for a considerable period of time before we arrived. We are here at the invitation of the Guatemalan Government to resolve a civil war crisis that's deteriorating. We have the Marines on video film with photographs and witness statements by the Indians of the villages. They came back with, 'Tell us more'. I could see they intended to use the information against the Americans. The C.O., who had been listening to the entire dialogue, took control of the radio.

We were told we were to go after the U.S. Marines, that our mission was still a priority, but scale down the booby traps, just scare them, don't injure or kill. In the end not a single soldier, American or British, was injured or killed but most important at that time, no more villages were wrecked and no more occupants injured or killed.

When moving to the next village, we had already chased the U.S. Marines out of five villages and were still four days in front and feeling pretty confident in ourselves. But everything was to change at that point, I was then surprised by information from the Indian villagers about the U.S. Marines. Nobody could find them anywhere, they had vanished.

Now the U.S. Marines had vanished, the linguist informed me of our invitation to come to a celebration feast with the Indians in the local village. After the food we had been eating for the last six weeks the talk of a 'feast' made our mouths drool in anticipation. Our food had been diabolical. Stuffed with proteins, carbohydrates and vitamins, but tasting awful. It was meant to reduce the overall load for the six weeks in Guatemala.

However, the biscuits were solid enough to break your teeth. The food bars tasted like shit, and many of the other men had long abandoned the diet in preference for the local food which the villagers were prepared to obtain and cook on our behalf. I would sooner have eaten a 'mars bar', but it showed a mark of respect for the Indian villagers, and a certain gratitude on their part for what we were doing.

When meeting the RAF helicopter, we were precisely on time and hiding in the jungle so that when he arrived all we had to do was walk out of the forest and we were standing around the helicopter, waiting to take off. We made a point about antagonising the pilot with comments like 'Well, what are we waiting for?'

Gradually Colin began to settle. He appreciated the Unit manager's thoughtfulness, and sat up all night watching the SNP win the election in 2016. He was completely elated that night/ week/month, and shared that with every person he came into contact with.

Eileen – the Unit manager – was very clear that the nursing home was Colin's home, and nothing was too much trouble. She looked at each person as an individual, and sought to enable people to keep their dignity and ability to choose. She saw beyond Colin's anger, to the scared, frustrated, damaged soul underneath, and she treated him with humour. When you asked Colin something like 'How are you? he would often growl back 'Stupid question.'

When Colin complied with a request, like taking his tablets, the cry might go up, 'Who are you, and what have you done with Colin?' because he was doing what was asked of him in taking his tablets, and so made himself seem like an imposter! The real Colin would usually not take his tablets, at least without much coaxing and cajoling.

Eileen told Colin one day that he was looking especially handsome, and Colin's instant reply was 'I know'. I was so grateful for such an enlightened attitude, that encouraged freedom of choice where possible, and where humour and banter were used to promote Colin's feeling of safety and wellbeing. There are so few units to care well for people age under 65 with disabilities, we need more.

Colin received a cooked breakfast every morning – i.e. any time between 10am till 4pm when Colin woke up – and this was greatly appreciated. Colin often kept the tablet beakers, and cut up the bacon rind and stored them in the beakers, and then got someone to put them out on the bird table outside his window. He loved watching the enormous pigeons come to eat. Colin was often bad tempered, but he loved when he got his way, and when people listened to his stories. He enjoyed the antics of the Unit's dog Murphy, and liked his company. He was often took a long supervised soak in a bubble bath, which he found very relaxing. He liked to tell people about his three dimensional chess set, but he did get very cross if someone bumped into it, or a piece went missing. Then we all had to crawl along the floor and search under the bed, and round the piles of dvds to look for it. Going into Colin's room was never dull!

Colin loved going out to coffee shops with Bill and Neil, and with myself. A decaf coffee and soup and panini and then ice cream seldom went wrong. And on a Friday night, his mum and dad came up, and the staff kindly gave them all a fish tea and pudding. Sometimes I would rush over to spend time with Colin for an hour between work appointments, and he would be asleep, and I would just sleep too. Other days, he was bright and wanting company, and chatting about the rugby or the latest political event, and then he was resentful that I didn't come more often.

Colin kept less well. He was admitted to hospital on a number of occasions – one time he was admitted to a local hospital with an unspecified infection. The staff at the nursing home went with him to A and E. I joined Colin there. However the problem with all these admissions is that Colin is unwell, and can't speak for himself. Medically there is often not much to look at – maybe a bit of a temperature spike, or a bit of a twitch or very drowsy, but it hardly looks like a major crisis. I have power of attorney, but too often staff just dismiss me as over anxious. And if I leave A and E, it gets worse, because nursing staff there or in a ward, will not discuss a patient's condition over the phone with someone else, power of attorney or not. Often when you visit the ward during the day, there is no doctor available to speak to you. So there is no one to speak for a vulnerable adult, unless you sleep on the floor in the ward beside them, and stay there every day, which is not very practicable. These policies are not in the best interest of vulnerable patients or their families.

I'm going to speak about two of Colin's hospital admissions as they feel so dramatic. On the first occasion, when Colin was admitted for an infection, you go into a hospital ward, and the nurse says brightly, 'He is much better today', and Colin is sleepy and emotional. I wonder what the nurse means. I look at his notes at the end of the bed, and they say he has been agitated in the night, and that it has taken four staff to hold him down and medicate him. Not that the staff would tell me this! Then the next day, I notice Colin's watch is broken, and lying on his table. Colin is still drowsy and unable to speak – all I can do is bring him ice cream, and feed him with a spoon. I wonder why his watch is broken. When there were no nurses about, one of the other patients said that Colin had fallen, but I wasn't to tell anyone that it was him who told me. When I ask the nurse, she doesn't know what has happened to Colin's watch.

Colin was on IV antibiotics, but his condition remained the same. He was given assistance to eat his food at mealtimes, but apart from that he slept, or opened his eyes but was generally unresponsive. This went on for days, with no sign of improvement.

Then out of the blue, a consultant – very apologetic. He had spoken to the physios, and discovered that Colin had fallen the previous week in the ward, but it wasn't written up in Colin's notes, because it was only the nurses who would normally write up the notes. As Colin had not been responsive for such a long time, they had therefore sent him for a head CT, and it was normal, so the fall wasn't the reason for his unresponsive state. I told the consultant I was aware that this might have happened, but that it was a patient that had told me – the nurse had denied it. I was grateful that the consultant had had the decency to follow this up and the courage to phone, but I was so unimpressed that ward communication was so bad that these incidents were not recorded, and even denied.

Another joy (code for incredible frustration) in this ward, was that the neurologist came round only on a Monday and Friday, as it was not a neurological ward. Colin was referred to see a neurologist, because of his lack of progress. His infection markers were still higher than they should be. The neurologist was to come the next day on Friday. I waited all Friday at the hospital – Colin was mainly asleep, although he smiled a little when I read from the newspaper. I asked the staff when the neurologist was coming, and at 4.45pm they said he probably wouldn't be coming now – he should come on Monday.

By Monday, there is no change. Then Colin has a seizure. I phone the ward, and they say the neurologist has been early, and he has put Colin's medication up. When I speak to the ward manager in person, she says the medication change was only a suggestion, and that it has still to be confirmed. Eventually I manage to speak to a consultant on the ward in person, who says it is difficult for consultants to liaise between different local authority hospitals, and that the computer portals are not compatible, so all the records are not available. They hadn't factored me into the conversation about Colin's medication, because in that ward they said they were not used to relatives taking such an active interest in their patients. The bottom line was that they felt that they had done all they could, and were now going to discharge Colin back to the care home.

Later in the same year, Colin was poorly again, with a chest infection. The phonecall came from the home at 4am – I always listen for my phone, even when I am asleep. Colin had had a seizure and his breathing was poor – an ambulance had been called. I got dressed, got into the car and went to A and E. Colin had aspirated. He is put on IV sodium valporate and warm oxygen to help his lungs.

I keep working, but visit every time I can. Colin has been admitted to HDU – he is not responding to treatment, and the doctors are very concerned for him. I phone round the family, and let them know. His blood pressure is down, and his oxygen levels are poor. He is on a very noisy oxygen mask and machine, but the consultant says he can only use this for 48 hours, as Colin's CO2 levels are getting too high. The consultant says I need to tell his family what is happening, and I phone round again. He says he will have to turn off the machine, and that Colin might not survive this.

I have to conduct a funeral at 3pm, and there is not time to get someone else to conduct it. I drive over to the crematorium with tears running down my face, praying to be composed enough to conduct the service. By the grace of God I manage, and the family just think I am very empathetic. Tears and death seem round every corner. I rush back, and they have taken Colin off the machine anyway, before I got back – despite saying they would wait till I got back. We sit round the bed, waiting and praying – for hours. His stats start to drop, but then they level out. By 10pm, Colin opens his eyes, and accuses the nurses of stealing his watch. Back to normal.

Whilst he was poorly, I sat and spoke to Colin of all he had done in his life, his military service, his travelling, his family – it brought back to me the richness of Colin's life, and all that he had achieved, and was strangely healing.

Colin again made very slow progress, on more antibiotics, barely eating, not very responsive. He was still not out of the woods, but was still with us. He was coughing away and very weak, but eating a little. There were long conversations with doctors re antibiotics, and medications for his seizures and to calm his mood, and the possible interactions. The psychiatrist was excellent, but everything needed such very careful handling. Colin was moved to another ward, where I visited at mealtimes, to try and get him to eat. There was a lovely Franciscan man in the bed opposite Colin, who said he would pray for Colin and watch over him when I wasn't there. It was like there was a beautiful angel in the room, and it was just so moving that another patient would show such care to us. Colin got back to the care home after a three week stay, very weak and moody, but still with us.

Back at the care home, Colin was often difficult, he had infections, his brain damage meant he could be loud and foul mouthed one moment, and then charming and apologetic the next. He made many friends, and loved being in his room with his music and dvds, often listening to praise music and enjoying the church service. He was particularly proud of Andrew, and his visits with the dog. They all played together beautifully, and we used to hide treats behind Colin's back, so the dog would sit and look at him attentively for hours!

One of Colin's proudest moments was knowing that Andrew had passed his test, and giving Andrew money towards his first car, and getting a ride in it – a wonderful day. Even though I worried that Andrew was driving too fast, Colin was elated to be driven by his son, and egged him on. It was a really emotional day, a mixture of pride and pathos. Colin looked so weak, but he was so pleased to see his son's progress.

Andrew loved his dad, but it was a hard road for him too – he wrote the following, just after his dad's death:

In some ways, daddy's condition terrified me as a child. I know he never meant it, but the injury made him act in ways that he wouldn't mean to, but which would come across as very strongly, to a child. Or even to an adult! This had some implications for me. sometimes I wanted to run away, when he shouted.

There is so much to try and put into words. We have memories of holidays, where despite his condition, dad tried to push the boundaries to try and do something. When he cycled in Millport, where he cycled, although he had not been on a bike for years, and had no balance,

On our trips to America, just physically surviving the trips over, and trying to keep cool despite his conditions – e.g. going through airport security.

It was difficult for me as a child, but it also gave me an insight like a skill set that no-one else would have, so young.

It was difficult growing up. I was inspired for justice and trying to do the right thing. It was so unfair for soldiers who came home after service. Even though on Remembrance day, people often talk about people who died in the war, but few people talk re their journey at home, without help. Surviving for 37 years, was a testament to his will, and was pretty impressive, almost more impressive than giving up your life.

Daddy inspired me to persevere, so many times he was told that he was going to die, and despite every obstacle, he would pull through, even when the doctors gave up on him.

In my early years, so much went on. I would like others to understand that you cannot understand what others go through, plenty of people said to me 'I know what it is like', but I knew that was completely unrealistic, and that they had no idea. Every chance you get to give to others, you need to take.

We did some nice things – going to the Science centre, playing crazy golf, learning to play chess – although he wasn't keen if someone else won.

Lots of memories – I thought of him as a true hero.

As time went on, Colin's moods became more erratic, his medication was reviewed, he was hospitalised from time to time. The psychiatrist Dr Thomas was excellent, and visited Colin himself, and treated him with dignity and great care. Colin's walking became poorer, and true to form, he was too proud and independent to use a stick, and so he fell many times, until he broke his hip. The partial hip replacement and infection made a recovery almost impossible, as Colin did not have the strength to walk again, despite physio. He became frailer, and took unwell in February with yet another infection – it was thought he only had days to live, so he was cared for palliatively in the care home. Being stubborn, Colin lasted 55 days, till he passed away peacefully, age 61, on 14th April 2018 with me at his side.

In that last February, I was told that Colin was very frail, and not making much progress. I could see that with my eyes. He needed specialist physios to help him to learn to walk again, who were trained to help people with diminished capacity. Yet when they came, he was often asleep or unresponsive. One day, Colin was so frustrated he sat and clomped his feet of the floor for hours so he would get better, but pure rage wasn't enough to do it. Colin spent much of his time in bed, and when he did sit up in a chair, it was hard because he was weak and cranky, with little energy to learn something new. Everyone did what they could, but Colin, despite his fierce determination, could not get his body to conform.

Just a week later, Colin had another infection, and he had lost his capacity to swallow, antibiotics were not working, and he had sepsis. It seemed cruel to treat him more aggressively, as he was already so frail. He was made comfortable. Colin was put on a low dose of morphine, his colour was poor, there were signs of seizure activity, at times Cheyne Stoke breathing – so alarming watching erratic breathing, wondering if each day would be Colin's last. His family came, a couple of friends, some ministers to pray with him.

By the end of the week, a certificate was written by the GP, to say that Colin's death was expected. I was meant to be on holiday, so no one was looking for me, so I kept vigil at his bedside. I prayed, and read and slept.

After the first week, Colin was still very poorly, but at times he seemed a little brighter. Colin barely spoke, unless he was sore, but you could tell by his eyes the times he was listening. He could not eat, but he managed some ice cream. He watched his favourite films – Independence Day, Bi-Centenial Man, Blue Planet and El Cid – or at least they were on in the back ground. The five nations rugby was on, and one of the only times Colin smiled was when I said that he looked a bit like Gavin Laidlaw!

In the midst of his frailty, Colin's heart kept beating. The snow came, and it was hard to get about. People gave me lifts to the care home. Our son Andrew gave some of the staff lifts, as the roads were so bad that they couldn't get in to work. Some days, Colin had seizures. He had problems swallowing his medication and more and more was given intravenously. On some surreal nights, the moon shone across the snow, and the light in the room was amazing, spilling out across his pillow.

I felt I couldn't go back to work – every day could have been Colin's last. Some days I would come in, and his colour was poor and he was very still. Sometimes he was restless and unsettled, and at least I could try to support him. Other days he seemed oblivious to all that was going on around him. Sometimes he just slept.

As the days went on, Colin became thinner, somehow his fingers seemed longer and more slender. The shape of his jaw was more pronounced. I would often sit and talk to Colin about his life – all the things he had achieved in the military, of his family life, of his courage. I read some of the psalms, we read 'Footprints'. I wanted to make his last days as full of love and care as possible. We listened to music – when Colin was brighter it was Runrig, or when he was quieter it was Mary Black or classical music or harp music. He had water on a wee sponge, so as not to choke. Some of the freshening sticks were lemon, which Colin liked, and he would try to keep it in his mouth as along as possible, which was not ideal! Some days were so disturbing – when pain broke through, and Colin would wince or scream when he was turned.

I wrote a prayer around this time:

Gracious God, Father, Son and Holy Spirit,

You have Colin's name written on the palm of your hand,

You know and love him – for Christ's sake have mercy on him.

You know Colin's suffering – his fragility, frustration, seizure activity,

In the midst of all this, may his thoughts turn to you,

That you might set him free from indignity and suffering,

And from the things that imprison him – regrets and worry.

In your perfect timing, bring him into your nearer presence,

A place of healing and restoration,

Where he can be free from incapacity, to dance and to sing your praises.

I am powerless, I surrender to you, please look in mercy on Colin,

And release him from his suffering.

In this time of cocoon, I feel I have sat in the tomb with death,

Yet you have stayed with me, strengthened my inner being, given me faithful, prayerful travelling companions, and strengthened me though your Holy Spirit.

Grant me strength for the days to come, and to tell this story, Amen.

In his final days, we had to take Colin's wedding ring off, as his fingers were so swollen. His jaw was slack, his breathing erratic, his colour changing regularly. He battled away, but there was little left of him. Sometimes there were shafts of sunlight across the bed. Everyone did all they could to make his comfortable, and in his last 24 hours, his mum and dad visited, and also Andrew. I gave him permission to go, if he needed to, and thanked him for being such a faithful and loyal husband and father.

We are so grateful for the excellent care that Colin received at Craigielea Care home, which made his final years fun and comfortable, in the midst of severe medical and behavioural problems. Eileen and her staff always treated Colin as a member of the family, and he grew to trust his feeling of acceptance and care, and even in his confusion and frustration, that made his final years so very enriching. There were many joyful moments along the way, getting his beautiful personalised birthday cakes, singing along to the 'singing santa' about Christmas being the most wonderful time of the year, meeting the reindeer, trying to throw his sensory mat in the bin when no-one was looking, chatting to Vin – one of the staff – and the others, eating enough cake to last forever. Even in the pain, so much to give thanks for. Colin lived a life of ferocious loyalty, courage and care, and was a valiant warrior, in this life and the life to come.

'Everything is beautiful in its time.'

Ecclesiastes 3

'I have fought the good fight, I have finished the race, I have kept the faith.'

2 Timothy 4:7

AFTERWORD

Every time I reread Colin's story – my eyes fill with tears. As a direct result of his injuries sustained during active service, Colin suffered tangibly and viscerally till the day he died. War has such a high cost, not just for the wounded, but for their families. Some days Colin just got on with things, other days he was upset and angry, full of frustration and self-loathing, and taking it out on these closest to him. Colin could be very scary, making lots of noise, talking as if he would harm you, for after all he was a trained killer, as he would remind you.

At times, the only way to cope, was to compartmentalise your life. To get on with work, and seeing family and friends, and putting on a mask. Yet now and again the phone would go – Colin was admitted to hospital with an infection, he had aspirated, he was on a machine to breathe for him. I had my phone with me everywhere, just waiting for it to ring. I would be conducting a church service, and would turn on the phone and there was an urgent call from the hospital, or had to postpone a holiday, as Colin's condition was unstable. You live on a constant adrenalin high, just waiting for the next bad news.

On other days, Colin was content – cutting the rind off his bacon to feed the birds. Or dancing with another resident at the church service. Or telling the night staff in great detail about the exhilaration of a parachute jump, and encouraging them to study Scottish history and politics. Or putting on his ridiculous fedora shaped hat and going out for extra ice cream. There was a lot of fun, and Colin's dry sense of humour meant that nothing was ever predictable. He would say something ridiculous to you, and then give you that big delighted smile.

I think one of the striking things too, was the courage that Colin demonstrated again and again – not just on active service, but in just trying to live each day with his injuries and disability. He was often angry, frustrated, felt that others had not done what he had asked, didn't understand, felt isolated and confused. Yet sometimes in the darkest days, he surprised you with a dry quip, or a look of recognition or a stubbornness that was his will to go on. His heroism was an integral part of his being, and continued to the day he died.

I cannot adequately convey the battle that Colin endured, in military service and afterwards as a veteran, to try to survive with some kind of meaning and integrity. These words are my paltry effort – my love song for this wounded veteran.

I give thanks for Colin's life, for his courage facing impossible odds, for his love even when he was frustrated and confused. His idealism never diminished, and he was proud of all the ways he sought to help others in his military career. Looking back however, I wonder if there are ways to support veterans and their families better, and the challenge is how to do this. I have written about some things that helped me along this journey – spiritual and practical, in case they help another person. For ultimately we are all on this journey together. May God bless all those who seek to support those with disabilities and difficult illnesses, and may their love and compassion make a difference.

In the midst of an intense and upside down life of volcanic eruptions and beautiful angels, I am deeply thankful for Colin's life and all he taught me. May we all be channels of love and grace, willing to learn from others, and to make this world a better place.

On the second anniversary of Colin's birthday in September, I am sitting at the café at Fintry Bay Millport, a place that Colin loved. The hills of Arran are called 'The Sleeping Warrior', and I have a beautiful view of them here. It is nearby that Andrew and I scattered Colin's ashes.

As I sit here, the sky is stormy and overcast. At times, I feel like this – enmeshed in a lattice of dark shapes and outlines. Yet then the rays of the sunshine break through, and everything changes.

It helps me recall that in the midst of the darker times, there has been so much light – seven rays of light have been:

- Learning more of what it means to value every human being
- Having new insight as to what is really important in life
- Experiencing the tender love of God in unexpected places
- Meeting some stunning and inspirational people along the way
- Discovering a new community
- Learning things, that might help encourage just one person in their struggles
- Learning that to love another human being, and to seek to put them first is one of the most inspirational and life transforming thing you can ever do.

May we always be open to love and unexpected graces even in the most unlikely places – and to have courage to speak of them – the light always shines!

Appendix 2

GLOSSARY OF MEDICAL TERMS

1   **PTSD Post Traumatic Stress Disorder** – being affected by trauma in such a way that it impedes your daily living and the world no longer feels safe.

2   **Organic Personality Disorder** – long or short term personality disturbance caused by a physical malfunction of the brain.

3   **Phenytoin** – an older anti-convulsant drug, that worked for Colin for many years, until its side effects became more pronounced.

4   **Neurontin** – one of the newer anti-convulsant drugs.

5   **Lamotrogine** – one of the side effects of this anti-convulsant is 'bright dreams'.

6   **Trileptal** – used as a secondary anti-convulsant, often as an add on therapy when other treatments have been unsuccessful.

7   **Quarriers** – the Centre for Epilepsy Assessment at Quarrier's Village, Bridge of Weir.

8   **Therapeutic** – effective.

9   **Temazepam** – a tranquiliser taken for anxiety and to help calm seizure activity.

10 **Haloperidol** – anti-psychotic medication.

11 **Keppra** – one of the newer anti-convulsants.

12 **Psychotic** – detached from reality in some way, e.g. being delusional or interpreting things very differently from those around you.

13 **EEG** – Electroencephalogram, a non-invasive test that records patterns in your brain.

14 **Complex partial status** – non convulsive status epilepticus characterised by long lasting stupor, unresponsiveness and some motor automatism.

15 **Phenobarbitone** – very old drug not commonly used because of its adverse and cumulative effects.

16 **Psychotic episodes** – intervals of time when a person does not relate to reality, including e.g. confusion, hallucinations etc.

17 **Tegretol retard** – an anti-convulsant.

18 **Postictal** – after a seizure.

19 **Vagus nerve stimulator** – a device that delivers electrical impulses to the vagus nerve, as an add on treatment for intractable epilepsy.

20 **Tertiary anti-convulsants** – a third layer of medications, when two anti-convulsants together have been unsuccessful.

21 **Diazepam** – a benzodiazepine used to treat anxiety and seizures.

22 **Buccal midazolam** – administered by syringe into the mouth, to stop and help prevent seizures.

23 **MSG** – Monosodium glutamate, the chemical often blamed for adverse symptoms.

24 **Taurine and magnesium** – supplements which can support brain function.

25 **Sacral cranial work** – gentle bodywork which can help promote the working of the nervous system.

26 **Upledger Institute** – promotes sacral cranial work and training, based in Palm Coast, Florida.

27 **CAT – computerized axial tomography.** These scans produce a cross-sectional photo of parts of the body.

28 **Lorazepam** – another drug for those with anxiety and seizures.

29 **Bletharatis** – inflammation of the eyelids.

30 **EMDR** – Eye Movement Desensitisation and Reprogramming.

31 **CBT** – Cognitive Behaviour Therapy.

Appendix 3

SPIRITUAL RESOURCES FOR THE WEARY

When you are trying to care for some-one who is unwell or has an incapacity, the carer can often become exhausted and drained. And so I offer some resources that encouraged me – they might not be for everyone, but at key moments, they spoke to my heart.

Some books I happened to be reading, which helped in different ways:

Streams in the Desert – Lettie Cowman

Hinds' Feet on High Places – Hannah Hurnard

When the Heart Waits – Sue Monk Kidd

The Other Side of Chaos – Margaret Silf

Lessons of the Heart – Patricia Livingston

Divine Beauty - John O'Donohue

The Blessing of Tears – Julie Sheldon

God Loves Broken People – Sheila Walsh

The Body Keeps the Score – Bessel Van der Kolk

Bible verses that encouraged me during times of illness and grieving:

'Weeping may come in the night, but joy comes in the morning.'
  Psalm 30:5

'My tears have been my food, both day and night.'   Psalm 42:3

'When I am afraid, I will trust in you.' Psalm 56:3

'Take courage, it is I. Do not be afraid.' Matthew 14:27

'My grace is sufficient for you, for my power is made perfect in weakness.'
  2 Corinthians 12:9

'Through deep waters, I will be with you.' Isaiah 43:2

'We walk by faith, not by sight.' 2 Corinthians 5:7

'My soul is overwhelmed to the point of death. Stay here and keep watch with me.' Matthew 26:3

'My times are in your hands.' Psalm 31:1

'For our light and momentary troubles are achieving for us an eternal glory that far outweighs them all. So we fix our eyes not on what is seen, but on what is unseen, since what is seen is temporary, but what is unseen is eternal.' 2 Corinthians 4:17-18

'The Spirit of the Sovereign Lord is on me,
    because the Lord has anointed me
    to proclaim good news to the poor.
He has sent me to bind up the brokenhearted,
    to proclaim freedom for the captives
    and release from darkness for the prisoners,
to proclaim the year of the Lord's favor
    and the day of vengeance of our God,
to comfort all who mourn,
    and provide for those who grieve in Zion—
to bestow on them a crown of beauty instead of ashes,
    the oil of joy instead of mourning,
and a garment of praise instead of a spirit of despair.' Isaiah 63:1-3

'Sorrowing but always rejoicing." 2 Corinthians 6:10

'In quietness and trust is your strength.' Isaiah 30:15

'Whether we live or die, we belong to the Lord.' Romans 14:8

'Father, if you are willing, remove this cup from me, yet not my will but your will.' Luke 22:42

'Wait for the Lord, be strong and take heart, and wait for the Lord.' Psalm 27:14

'Why are you downcast, O my soul, why so disturbed within me? Put your hope in God, for I will yet praise him, my saviour and my God.' Psalm 42:5

'He will cover you with His feathers;
 under His wings you will find refuge;
His faithfulness is a shield and rampart.' Psalm 91:4

'Those who hope in the LORD will renew their strength. They will soar
 on wings like eagles; they will run and not grow weary, they will walk
 and not be faint.' Isaiah 40:31

'Do not be afraid - you are worth more than many sparrows.'
 Matthew 10:31

'My flesh and my heart may fail,
 but God is the strength of my heart and my portion forever.'
 Psalm 73:26

'He was despised and rejected by men,
 a man of sorrows and familiar with suffering,
Like one from whom men hide their faces,
 he was despised and we esteemed him not.
Surely he took up our infirmities, and carried our sorrows,
 Yet we considered him stricken by God, smitten by him and afflicted.
But he was pierced for our transgressions, he was crushed for our
 iniquities, the punishment that brought us peace was upon him,
 and by His wounds we are healed.' Isaiah 53:3-5

'The Lord your God is with you, he is mighty to save
 he will take delight in you, he will quiet you with His love,
 he will rejoice over you with singing." Zephaniah 3:17

'Jesus went though Galilee, teaching in their synagogues, preaching the
 good news of the kingdom, and healing every disease and sickness
 amongst the peoples.' Matthew 4:2

'Come to me, all you who are weary and heavy burdened, and I will give
 you rest. Take my yoke upon you and learn from me, for I am gentle and
 humble in heart, and you will find rest for my souls. For my yoke is easy
 and my burden is light.' Matthew 11:28-30

'Take courage. It is I – do not be afraid.' Matthew 14:27

'Jesus got up, rebuked the wind and said to the waves, "Quiet, be still".'
 Mark 4:39

'Jesus wept.' John 11:35

'Praise be to the God and father of the Lord Jesus Christ, the Father of compassion and the God of all comfort, who comforts us in all our troubles, so we can comfort those in any trouble with the comfort we ourselves have received from God. For just as the sufferings of Christ flow into our lives, so also through Christ, our comfort overflows.' 2 Corinthians 1:3-5

'May the God of hope fill you with all joy and peace as you trust in him, so that you may overflow with hope by the power of the Holy Spirit.' Romans 15:13

'Praise be to the God and father of our Lord Jesus Christ, who has blessed us in the heavenly realms with every spiritual blessing in Christ.' Ephesians 1:3

'Do not be anxious about everything, but in everything, by prayer and petition, with thanksgiving, present your requests to God.' Philippians 4:6-7

'Be joyful always, pray continually, give thanks in all circumstances, for this is God's will for you in Jesus Christ.' 1 Thessalonians 5:16-18

'May the Lord direct your hearts into God's love and Christ's perseverance.' 2 Thessalonians 3:5

Songs to listen to when you feel at the bottom of the pit. On these darkest days – these artists, and many more – became like my friends on the journey!

When you want to be left alone to be miserable – Mandisa, *Just cry*

Trying to trust in the midst of pain and despair – Tim Hughs, *When the tears fall*

Just miserable – Rend Collective, *Weep with me*

The idea that after all the tears, there could still be love – Andrew Peterson, *After the last tear falls*

In the deepest darkness, there could one day be light – Andrew Peterson, *The dark before the dawn*

When you feel that you have failed, and you want to give up – Andrew Peterson, *Be kind to yourself*

When the world feels hostile, being with God is our safe house – Andrew Peterson, *My one safe place*

When you are hurting – Jason Gray, *Love will have the final word*

In the midst of frustration and nothing making sense – Jason Gray, *Even this will be made beautiful*

When you feel scared – Rob Gardner, *Nothing to fear*

When nothing works, and you just have to rely on God – Hillsong, *I surrender*

When feeling like I am tired and inadequate, and can't do anymore – Lauren Daigle, *You say*

When feeling like the world has no meaning – Lauren Daigle, *Love like this*

When so tired, you can't stand up – Lauren Daigle, *Rescue*

When I am hurting, please sit with me and don't give me platitudes – Jason Gray, *Not right now*

God never forsakes us – Matt Redman, *Never once*

When you are exhausted, and nothing makes any sense – Laura Story, *Nearness*

Even when things fall apart – again – God is calling us to trust him – Casting Crowns, *Praise you in the storm*

When you have lost hope, and you need encouragement to keep going – Casting Crowns, *Courageous*

When you are tired just trying to support everyone else – Casting Crowns, *Just be held*

When you have waited so long, but part of you still hopes – Danny Cokey, *Haven't seen it yet?*

When you are too tired to do anything but rest in God's love – Elevation Worship, *With you (Paradoxology)*

When the world seems to be falling apart, God keeps us safe – Elevation Worship, *For a moment*

Can something good come from the pain? – Laura Story, *Blessings*

I am trying too hard, and it's not working – Laura Story, *Grace*

I don't need to pretend everything is ok, when I am with God – Laura Story, *Peace*

When I feel afraid, your love crashes over me – Bethel Music, *You make me brave (Live)*

God has written a song just for me – Bethel music, *We dance (Live)*

God discovers me in my brokenness and brings healing – Jason Gray, *Learning to be found*

When I am so miserable and nothing is working out, I still trust – Mercy Me, *Even if*

Hope of beauty from the ashes – The Afters, *Broken Hallelujah*

Whatever happens, even if I fail, God still keeps hold of me – Laura Story, *He will not let go*

God is still here – Michael Card, *Never will I leave you*

When I feel lost and alone – Michael Card, *I will bring you home*

You are faithful, even when I struggle – Sarah Reeves, *Faithful*

Let me not be distracted from loving You, God – Sarah Reeves, *Just want you*

When people around you are discouraging – Francesca Battistelli, *Giants fall*

When prayer is not answered, I need to still cling on – Lauren Daigle, *Trust in you*

When I am hurting, I don't need to move, for God seeks me out – Laura Story, *You came running*

Making the right choice – Yvonne Lyon, *Again*

When you feel alone – Yvonne Lyon, *Lonely road*

When you are struggling – Yvonne Lyon, *All is not lost*

In the midst of the mess – Yvonne Lyon, *I am loved*

When things don't make sense, but at least you are still here –Mercy Me, *The hurt and the healer*

When it seems too long to wait – Stoneleigh Worship Band, *We have sung our songs*

Waiting and trusting – Laura Story, *Whisper*

Songs to listen to, when a little light seems possible:

Even yet, something good might come from this – Nichole Nordeman, *Something out of me*

Every detail can bring meaning – Nichole Nordeman, *Every mile mattered*

There is something more to this, than just suffering – maybe there can be a positive direction – Nichole Nordeman, *Listen to your life*

Out of brokenness, there can be new beginnings – Danny Cokey, *Tell your heart to beat again*

Just because you feel desolate and broken, doesn't mean you are not loved – Danny Cokey, *Wanted*

Desiring to tell your story, but not knowing where to start – Nicole Nordeman, *Sound of surviving*

When you need to be reminded you have stamina – Matthew West, *Never give up*

God is still faithful, even when it doesn't feel like it – Natalie Grant, *Never miss a beat*

In the midst of it all, there is still hope – Danny Cokey, *Hope in front of me*

Trusting – Lou Fellingham, *Wholly yours*

Trusting when there is no sense - again - Lauren Daigle – *Trust in you*

Relief – it is ok to let go and to trust – Laura Story, *I can just be me*

God gives me strength and courage to get out of the boat – We the kingdom, *Dancing on the waves (Live)*

There is some sense in it all even when it doesn't seem to make sense! – Jason Gray, *Nothing is wasted*

Somehow I am still a real person – Jason Gray, *Be your own kind of beautiful*

When I don't know who I am any more, only a carer – Jason Gray, *Remind me who I am*

When I feel weak, you call me back to your side – Hillsong United, *Even when it hurts*

God can breathe life into my tired soul, and give me new life – Jason Gray, *New way to live*

After everything, God can form something new out of my life – Jason Gray, *Love's not done with you*

I have learned from this, as God has put me back together – Jason Gray, *I will rise again*

When things are tough, God still holds our hand – Jason Gray, *A way to see in the dark*

God gives me strength to persevere (and dance) – Mandisa, *Overcomer*

Scars and brokenness tell their own story – Mandisa, *What scars are for*

God is amazing, in the midst of it all – Laura Story, *Extraordinary*

God is creating something new out of the pain – Casting Crowns, *In the hands of the Potter*

In the midst of it all, you call me to still know joy – Mandisa, *I hope you dance*

Sometimes we need to speak, welcome or not – Best Friends, *Born for this (Esther)*

It is ok to be me – Francesca Battistelli, *Free to be me*

I need to have the courage to tell our story – Francesca Battistelli, *Write your story*

In the midst of it all, the miracle is that God still loves us – Lauren Daigle, *Love like this*

Retreats and self care possibilities:

The Bield at Blackruthven at Tibbermore, Perth

Christian Healing ministries, Jacksonville, Florida, USA.

Ignatian Spirituality centre, 35 Scott Street, Glasgow,

Trauma therapies:

e.g. EMDR (Eye Movement Desensitisation and Reprogramming)

www.capacitar.org

Osteopathic support and cranial osteopathy:

e.g. Anna Potter, 34 George Street, Glasgow (text 07734439348)

Possible questions to ask in a medical setting:

What right do patients and their families have, when the patient has epilepsy, brain injury or lacks capacity? Let's be well informed to make decisions.

Ask for information about your loved one's condition

Ask to speak to the doctor about what is happening, what is going on, what the plan is? To question why?

Be confident in telling the doctor/nurse what the context is and what your concern is – you know your loved one's history, in a way the medical staff do not.

On a ward, ask to speak to the consultant, and ask for information. Also make clear if you have power of attorney, to make sure that this is marked on the notes, and to ensure that there are arrangements for good communication. Keep telling everyone you have POA – if you have, you can ask to see the notes.

Feed in information that might not be available – e.g. to check the record of medication is up to date

If you are not sure, ask for a second opinion.

Organisations and Websites which may have helpful information:

NHS Scotland – you can read the Charter of Patient Rights and Responsibilities on your local NHSS website

Patient Advice and Support Service – 08009172127 offers confidential support and advice on health related matters in NHS Scotland

You can ask for advice from local patients support groups

Care opinion UK – feed your story to this non profit feedback platform for health and social care, to make services better

Scottish Independent Advocacy Alliance 0131 510 9410

Charter of patients rights and responsibilities

Epilepsy connections, Baltic Chambers, Suites 129-134, 50 Wellington Street, Glasgow G2 6DH, 0141 248 4125

Tom Allan Centre, 22 Elmbank St, Glasgow G2 4PB, 0141 221 1535.

Specific Veteran's resources:

Veteran's champions are officials who have volunteered to support veterans within the NHS and local councils. They are worth contacting for support. **Note:** All veterans should have the code 13JY on their notes for NHS care, which activates a covenant for priority treatment for all ex service personnel

Veteran's Gateway, 0808 802 1212 – signposts veterans and their families to different types of support (this could include e.g. Combat Stress, Veterans with dogs, Coming Home centre etc)

The Coming Home centre, 840 Govan Road, Govan, G51 3UU, 0141 237 8830.

A Particular Book

The Body Keeps the Score by Bessel van der Kolk has challenged me as to different ways to support those with trauma. The use of ACE courses (Adverse Childhood Experience) and trauma informed care, and First Aid in Mental Health courses, is very positive in educating people, and making us more aware of how to help people who are struggling and feel overwhelmed.

My understanding is that EMDR[*30] and CBT[*31] (see Appendix 2) are therapies which can address some of the symptoms of trauma in an effective way.

If you wish to contact the author directly, use:
woundedwarriorfg@gmail.com